"Open your eyes
and the whole world
is filled with God."

Sincerely,

Weldon Boone

June, 1965

PASSING THE LAURELS. A sketch by David Hunter Strother showing wilderness conditions in 1852. From David Hunter Strother, *Virginia Illustrated: Containing a Visit to the Virginian Canaan, and the Adventures of Porte Crayon (pseudo.) and his Cousins.* New York. Harper & Brothers. 1857.

A HISTORY OF BOTANY IN WEST VIRGINIA

BY WELDON BOONE
PRINCIPAL, HINTON HIGH SCHOOL
HINTON, WEST VIRGINIA

McCLAIN PRINTING COMPANY
PARSONS, WEST VIRGINIA 26287

1965

McCLAIN PRINTING COMPANY
PARSONS, W. VA. 26287

Library of Congress Catalog Card Number 63-22682
PRINTED IN THE UNITED STATES OF AMERICA

FOR

KATHRYN DAYLE

AND

DAVID WESLEY

Acknowledgements

Grateful acknowledgement is hereby made to the many persons who have helped to make this publication possible. I am especially grateful to Dr. Earl L. Core for his guidance in the selection and organization of botanical data; for the use of his personal library; for his help in preparing the index; for editing the manuscript and for general assistance in its publication.

I am indebted to the following persons for their interest and cooperation in facilitating this publication: Miss Elizabeth Ann (Betty) Bartholomew, curator of the Herbarium, West Virginia University, for furnishing names and addresses and data concerning many botanists; Mrs. Gladys Parker Boone, the author's wife, for her encouragement and useful suggestions; Mrs. Thelma Sullenberger Hyson, of Pt. Marion, Pa., and Anchorage, Alaska, for her careful preparation of typescript.

I am grateful to the following persons for their review and criticism of the manuscript: Mrs. Clyde A. Johnson, English teacher at Hinton High School, Hinton, West Virginia; Mrs. Kathryn Suzanne Boone Isner, the author's daughter, English teacher at Forest Hill High School, Forest Hill, West Virginia; Miss Ada Thompson, English teacher at Charleston High School, Charleston, West Virginia; Miss Nellie Cundiff, faculty member at Hinton High School, Hinton, West Virginia; Mr. Julian K. Whanger, Deputy Comptroller of the State of New York, Albany, New York. I also wish to thank Dr. H. L. Barnett and Dr. J. G. Leach, of the Department of Plant Pathology, West Virginia University, for information relative to the history of mycology, and Mr. W. H. Gillespie and I. S. Latimer, Sr., of the Department of Geology, West Virginia University, for permission to use a portion of their history of paleobotany.

I wish to thank scores of the botanists mentioned in the publication for their biographical data, furnished to the author through personal interviews or questionnaires.

I am also indebted to West Virginia University and to the McClain Printing Company, Parsons, W. Va., for their help in bringing the publication of this work to a reality.

Foreword

This book, the product of a labor of love on the part of its author, should serve numerous purposes. It is a contribution to the general history of West Virginia, and it is at the same time a contribution to the history of education in West Virginia. It is far more than a collection of biographies of West Virginia botanists, although it is that, too: in a sense it is a bibliography of West Virginia botany. That it is a thorough treatment of the subject is attested by the fact that the index lists references to approximately 500 persons associated with the development of botany in this State. In addition, hundreds of titles of books and articles dealing with the botany of the State are listed. It is, itself, a valuable contribution to the botanical literature of West Virginia.

Earl L. Core

Table of Contents

CHAPTER I

Botanical Exploration Before 1863

John Muir, the famous naturalist, was so impressed by the Appalachian flora, he said: "No matter what man may do to or say about the Appalachian Forests, God surely loved them for they are the most beautiful he ever made." This publication gives a brief account of the development of botany in a most interesting portion of this region, now known as West Virginia. It is very difficult for us today to visualize the wilderness conditions that existed here two hundred or even one hundred years ago. Conditions as they existed then are well portrayed by "The Blackwater Chronicle," a narrative of a trouting excursion through "Canaan Valley" to Blackwater Falls, Tucker County, by five "adventurous gentlemen" in 1851. This party included the narrator, Philip Pendleton Kennedy ("The Clerke of Oxenforde"), and David Hunter Strother ("Porte Crayon"), who drew numerous illustrations. These sketches are among the oldest known pictures of conditions in the original wilderness of this area. The writer of this most interesting account of the expedition states:

> "Pursuing the Northwestern road some three miles, we reached the top of the Backbone ridge. Here, turning at right-angles to the left, we followed a mountain-road along the top of the ridge for some miles, which at length took its course along the eastern side of the mountain; gradually growing into a mere single horse-track, until we reached Conway's house, the last settlement in this direction. Here we picked up Conway, with his rifle and frying-pan; and after a walk of some six miles or more through a most noble forest of sugar-trees, the beech, maple, wild-cherry, balsam-firs, and hemlocks, and over tracts of land wonderfully fertile, judging by the great size of the trees, and the growth of the wild timothy upon one or two slight clearings we passed through, we at length descended into a beautiful little glade—more properly a dale in the mountains—some three hundred yards wide and two or three miles long, where we were to turn out our horses to pasture until our return.

> "This dale is girt round upon its edges by a broad belt of the *Rhododendron*—commonly called the *big laurel* out here—which makes a dale of safe enclosure for keeping our horses; for it is impossible that a horse can make his way through it, so thick and lapped together everywhere are its branches. We had to enter it by a path cut for the purpose. When within, we barricaded the entrance by piling up some young trees and brushwood (which was equivalent to putting up the bars in a fenced field), and rode on down the middle of the wild meadow, through green grass, knee-high, and waving gently in the summer wind, until we reached a small stream, whose banks were overgrown with osiers and other delicate shrubs."[1]

They proceeded on foot into the wilderness toward Blackwater Falls.

> "The wilderness was growing wilder. We had, some time since, lost all trace of anything like even a deer-path . . . Now we had to climb some steep hill-side, clinging to the undergrowth to pull ourselves up, and now we would come up against a barrier of fallen trees—some of them six feet high as they lay along the ground, and coated with moss half a foot thick—some so decomposed that they recreated themselves in the young hemlocks and firs that grew up out of them—some more recently fallen, and great mounds of earth and stone heaved up with their roots; these mounds sometimes covered over by other trees thrown across them, and thus affording shelter to the wild animals from the snows and storms of winter. Over all these we would climb and roll ourselves across; and sometimes, such obstruction did they present to our course, we would be obliged to make a detour round for the length of a quarter of a mile may be, and find ourselves only advanced a hundred paces on the straight line of our route. It was thus we went along—up-hill and down—now along the side of a rib of the mountain—now over its cone, and now along it—down through deep ravines and up out of them, and scarcely able at any time to see further ahead than some twenty yards, so thick were the leaves about us; and not often able to catch a glimpse of the sun, so thick was the mass of foliage *umbrellaed* out everywhere above us."[2]

[1]Philip Pendleton Kennedy, "The Blackwater Chronicle," New York: Redfield, 1853, pp. 88-90.

[2]Ibid, pp. 109-110.

During the following summer of 1852, several of the same party, with other friends, made a second expedition into the same area, and this is described by Strother. Excerpts from his account of the excursion, illustrating the wilderness conditions follow:[3]

> "The gloom of the forest around was intense; the campfire blazed in the centre of a group of four lofty firs, whose straight and mast-like trunks were illuminated by its light for a hundred feet without the interruption of a limb, and whose tops interlaced and formed a lofty and almost impervious covering over the sleepers . . . The bodies of these fallen giants afforded quite a curious spectacle as they lay prone and supine, singly and in monstrous heaps, frequently a hundred and fifty feet in length and eighteen in girth, coated with a rich covering of moss, and their decayed wood affording a soil for thickets of seedlings of their own and other species . . . The hunters had been dodging the laurel-brakes all day. They seemed to dread the passage, and would frequently go miles around to avoid it. They had stories of men who had spent days in them, wandering in circles, and who had finally perished from starvation; and they say when once fairly in there is no calculating when you will get out. Some of these brakes extend for many miles, and are so dense that even the deer can not pass except by finding the thinnest places; and when the experienced woodman is forced to cross, he always seeks a deer-path. The ponderous strength of the bear enables him to traverse them more easily. In them he makes his lair; and our adventurers often found the laurel recently torn and broken by bears in going to and from their places of retreat . . . The laurel waved up and down as far as the eye could reach, like a green lake, with either shore walled by the massive forest, and out of its bed rose single, or in groups of three or four, the tallest and most imposing of the fir species."

The earliest botanical explorers in what is now West Virginia were Europeans who resided in Pennsylvania, Virginia, and the Carolinas. Apparently the main purpose of their travels was to find new plants in the unexplored wilderness to be sold on the European markets, although some botanical specimens were

[3]David Hunter Strother, "Virginia Illustrated: Containing a Visit to the Virginian Canaan, and the Adventures of Porte Crayon (pseud.) and His Cousins," New York: Harper and Brothers, 1857, pp. 25-30.

preserved. They were doubtless well repaid for their efforts by finding such showy shrubs as azaleas, rhododendrons, silverbells, and fringe trees. It is likely that their travels brought them within the eastern borders of the State. It is very difficult to determine their collecting stations in West Virginia, as most of their notes and labels read simply "Virginia." Prior to 1784 Virginia extended from the Atlantic to any point beyond the Ohio River, and the boundaries of West Virginia were not established until 1863. It was impossible for the early botanical explorers to designate the exact place of collections due to the fact that the country was so sparsely settled and localities so uncertainly named.

Among the early explorers were Peter Kalm, John Fraser, John Clayton, and John Mitchell. Peter Kalm, one of the students of Linnaeus, explored in Pennsylvania. *Kalmia latifolia,* the State Flower of Pennsylvania, was discovered by him and named for him by Linnaeus. Clayton is said to have traveled "to the Mississippi"; perhaps the Kanawha, in the Mississippi drainage.

In the latter part of the eighteenth century and early part of the nineteenth century, as settlement became more stabilized, numerous botanical studies were made.

Andre Michaux (1746-1802), the renowned French botanist, made numerous journeys, under conditions of great danger and hardships, along the borders of West Virginia. On his journey to Kentucky and Illinois in 1793 he collected at Harpers Ferry, Charles Town, and Summit Point, in Jefferson County, and at Wheeling, Buffalo Point, and the mouth of the Little Kanawha River. His collections are in the herbarium of the Museum of Paris. (See his "Flora Boreali-Americana sistens Caracteres Plantarum quas in America septentrionali collegit et detexit," 2 vols., 1803; also extracts from his journal.)

Matthias Kin, a German nurseryman and collector, while residing in Germantown, Pennsylvania, traveled extensively in the Allegheny Mountains. He often dressed as an Indian and became known as the "Indian plant-hunter." The main purpose of these excursions was to collect living plants and seeds for horticultural purposes, although he also preserved plants for herbarium specimens. One of the interesting specimens collected by Kin, about the year 1800, was a plant which he labelled *Coronopus tripitus,* but which was recognized by Thomas Nuttall as being *Carex fraseri.* This collection was made "in Deigher walli in der wilternus." This has been interpreted by

West Virginia state flower, *Rhododendron maximum,* used here through the courtesy of H. P. Sturm of Clarksburg, W. Va.

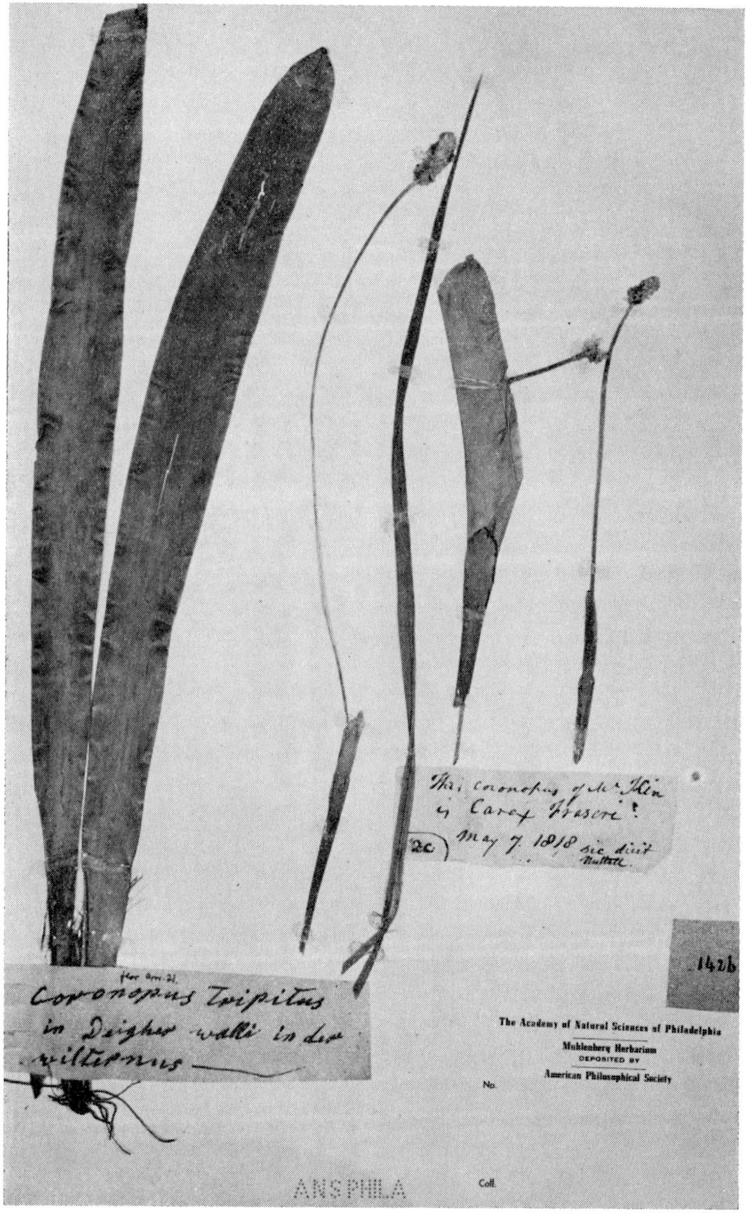

Fig. 1. Carex fraseri. Photograph of the original specimen collected by Matthias Kin (courtesy of Dr. C. Earle Smith, Jr., Academy of Natural Sciences, Philadelphia).

Asa Gray and others as doubtless referring to Tygarts Valley, in what is now West Virginia. Some of his collections were sent back to the herbarium of the Berlin Botanical Garden, and were presumably destroyed by a bomb on March 1, 1943, during World War II. He also had duplicate specimens in Philadelphia at the Academy of Natural Science. A specimen of *Carex fraseri* is still there. It is interesting to note that no other known collection of this plant was made in Tygarts Valley until June 21, 1963, when John L. Findley and Arden R. Swecker found it about 6 mi. south of Huttonsville.

Frederick Pursh (1774-1820), a noted German botanist, located in Philadelphia in 1799, and from there made important botanical explorations into the Alleghenies. His most interesting collection was made in 1805 in the vicinity of Harpers Ferry, Jefferson County, White Sulphur Springs, Greenbrier County, and Sweet Springs, Monroe County. His collections are in the Royal Botanical Gardens at Kew, London. (See his "Flora Americana septentrionalis," 2 vols., 1814; also Edgar T. Wherry, "Heuchera hispida Pursh rediscovered," *Rhodora* 35:118-119. 1933.)

Constantine Samuel Rafinesque, an eccentric naturalist of Franco-German-Greek ancestry, was born October 22, 1783 in Turkey and came to Philadelphia in 1802. In 1818, on his way to Kentucky, he collected plants at Wheeling, Williamstown, and Point Pleasant, and on a return trip collected from Wheeling to Kenilworth in Ohio, Brooke and Hancock counties. In 1819 he collected along the Potomac River from Harpers Ferry to Cumberland, Maryland, through Jefferson, Berkeley, Morgan and Hampshire counties. In 1825 he again collected from Valley Grove to Wheeling in Ohio County, and later, starting from Cumberland, he followed the South Branch of the Potomac from its mouth through Hampshire, Hardy, and Pendleton counties, where he "collected many fine plants." In 1832 he again collected near Harpers Ferry. His collections which no doubt were large and valuable were mostly lost. (See R. E. Call, "Life and Writings of Rafinesque" 1895.) He died in 1840.

Benjamin Smith Barton was born February 10, 1766, in Lancaster, Pennsylvania. He was educated in Pennsylvania, Great Britain, and Germany. He taught botany, natural history, and medicine in Philadelphia from 1789 to 1815. He wrote books on a variety of subjects, including "Elements of Botany" (1803), the first botanical textbook published by an American; "Collections for an Essay towards a Materia Medica of the United States" (1798-1804), his chief medical work, dealing with medicinal plants based largely on original investigation; and the first part of a "Flora virginica," a reprint and elaboration of Clayton's work.

In 1802 he observed and collected plants in the Eastern Panhandle, while on a visit to Virginia. He also manifested his great interest in botany by financing explorations of Frederick Pursh and Thomas Nuttall. He died in 1815. (See "Journal of Benjamin Smith Barton on a Visit to Virginia, 1802," edited by W. L. McAtee, *Castanea* 3:85-117. 1938.)

Thomas Nuttall, botanist and ornithologist, was born at Settle, Yorkshire, on January 5, 1786. In 1808 he emigrated to Philadelphia, and was soon introduced to the study of plants by the Philadelphia botanist, Benjamin Smith Barton. He at once began the investigation of the native flora, extending his explorations southward to Maryland, Virginia, North Carolina, Mississippi and Florida. He collected at Harpers Ferry in 1818, where he noted the rare *Paronychia virginica,* and along the Ohio River on his way to the west. It is said that no other North American botanical explorer made more discoveries.

Among his contributions to botany are "The Genera of North American Plants, and a Catalogue of the Species, to the year 1817" (1818), and his continuation (vols. IV-VI, 1842-49) of "The North American Sylva" of F. A. Michaux.

Starting in 1822 he was curator of the Botanical Garden at Harvard University for ten years. He died in 1859.

William E. A. Aiken of Baltimore, Maryland, collected in the vicinity of Harpers Ferry, Jefferson County, about 1832. The extent and disposition of his collections are apparently not known.

Asa Gray (1810-1888), with **John Carey** and **John Constable,** on a collecting trip to the mountains of southwestern Virginia and North Carolina in 1841, passed through Jefferson County. Dr. Gray and **William Starling Sullivant,** in 1843 collected from Maryland to Georgia. Their route extended through St. George to the Tygarts Valley near Beverly, then along the Staunton and Parkersburg Pike across Cheat Mountain, where *Aconitum reclinatum* was found, by way of Cheat Bridge and Travelers Repose, and then south to Minnehaha Springs and east to Warm Springs, and south to Big Spring, Mercer County. Their specimens are in the Gray Herbarium of Harvard University. (See Core, Earl L. "Travels of Asa Gray in Western Virginia, 1843." *Rhodora* 42:344-351. 1940.)

Isaac Farwell Holton collected rather extensively from Charleston, Kanawha County to Hawks Nest, Fayette County, in October, 1849. His private collection is deposited in the herbarium of the New York Botanical Garden.

William Henry Brewer, while serving as professor of botany at Yale University, in 1860, made a collection of plants near Wheeling in Ohio County and near Bethany in Brooke County. His specimens are in the Yale University Herbarium.

REFERENCES

BERKELEY, EDMUND AND DOROTHY SMITH BERKELEY. "John Clayton: Pioneer of American Botany." 236 p. Chapel Hill. 1963.

CLARKSON, ROY B. "Fraser's Sedge, Cymophyllus fraseri (Andrews) Mackenzie." *Castanea* 26:129-136. 1961.

CORE, EARL L. "The Botanical Exploration of West Virginia," *Proc. W. Va. Acad. Sci.* 10:46-60. 1936.

CORE, EARL L. "Outlines of the Flora of West Virginia." Morgantown: West Virginia University Bookstore, 1954.

CORE, EARL L. "Plant Life in West Virginia." New York: Scholar's Library, 1960.

EWAN, JOSEPH. "Frederick Pursh and his Botanical Associates." *Proc. Am. Phil. Soc.* 96:599-628. 1952.

HARSHBERGER, JOHN W. "The Botanists of Philadelphia and Their Work." Philadelphia: T. C. Davis & Sons, 1899.

HUMPHREY, HARRY BAKER. "Makers of North American Botany." Ronald Press, New York. 1961. 265 p. (articles on Barton, Gray, Michaux, Nuttall, Pursh, and Rafinesque).

KENNEDY, PHILIP PENDLETON. "The Blackwater Chronicle," New York: Redfield, 1853.

MILLSPAUGH, C. F. "Botanical Field Work in the State." Pages 2-13 in West Virginia Geological Survey 5(A). Wheeling: Wheeling News Litho. Company, 1913.

PENNELL, F. W. "Travels and Scientific Collections of Thomas Nuttall." *Bartonia* 18:1-51. 1936.

RODGERS, ANDREW D., III. "Noble Fellow: William Starling Sullivant." Putnam's. New York. 1940.

STROTHER, DAVID HUNTER. "Virginia Illustrated: A Visit to the Virginian Canaan." New York: Harper & Brothers, 1857.

CHAPTER II

Botany From 1863 to 1889

Previous to the formation of the State of West Virginia on June 20, 1863, botanical explorations and other botanical work in what is now West Virginia was confined to persons from outside the State. With the establishment of the Agricultural College of West Virginia by the State Legislature on February 7, 1867, changed to West Virginia University on December 4, 1868, botany became a course of instruction and botanical explorations by West Virginians were made.

At the University during the first school term **Samuel G. Stevens** was professor of natural sciences. He was a native of New England and a graduate of Dartmouth College. He gave lectures to first-year agriculture students on "the chemistry, structure and physiology of plants" and second-year agricultural students also received a course in botany. There were no departments as designated today, and the courses were listed under the "Agricultural Department." Mr. Stevens might be considered the first teacher of botany at West Virginia University. For the second term, 1868-69, Mr. Stevens' title was changed to professor of natural philosophy and of the natural sciences. In addition to the two courses offered the first year for agriculture students a botany course was added for first-year students in the Science Department during the spring term. The textbook used was Gray's *School and Field Book of Botany.* The third year, 1869-70, Mr. Stevens' connection with botany was terminated and he was made professor of astronomy and physics and secretary of the University. He left the University after serving as vice president for four years.

During the school term 1869-70, the work in botany was handled by Dr. **John James Stevenson,** who was professor of chemistry and natural history, and botany was offered to sophomores this year during the spring term. Dr. Stevenson was born in New York, N. Y., October 10, 1841, and received his collegiate training at New York University. He received the bachelor of arts degree in 1863, the master of arts degree in 1866, and the doctor of philosophy degree in 1867. Dr. Stevenson continued at the University in the 1870-71 term, and in

1871 became professor of geology at New York University, where he remained until his retirement, being professor of geology until 1882, and then professor of chemistry and physics from 1882 to 1889, professor of geology and biology from 1889 to 1894, and professor of geology again from 1894 to 1909, when he became professor emeritus. He was awarded the doctor of laws degree by Princeton University in 1893, and by Washington and Jefferson College in 1902. He died August 10, 1924.

William Morris Fontaine handled the botany courses from 1872 to 1877 and had the title of Professor of Agriculture, Chemistry, and Natural History. He was born December 1, 1835, in Louisa County, Virginia. He received the master of arts degree at the University of Virginia in 1859, and studied in the Royal School of Mines, Freiburg, Saxony, in 1869-70. He served as lieutenant in the Confederate Army during the Civil War.

Professor Fontaine, during his first year at the University, gave a course in botany during the spring term for students in the School of Chemistry and Natural History, with Gray's *School and Field Book* as a text, and also a course entitled botany and vegetable physiology, for first-year students in the Agricultural Department. Professor Fontaine continued to offer the same botany courses, but the "School of Chemistry and Natural History" was changed to the "Scientific Department." For the 1877-78 term his title was changed to professor of agriculture, chemistry and physics, and his botany duties were taken over by Israel C. White, who was appointed professor of astronomy and natural history. In 1878, Mr. Fontaine accepted a position as professor of geology and natural history at the University of Virginia, retaining the position until 1911. He died April 29, 1913. While at West Virginia University Professor Fontaine taught his botany classes in Martin Hall until the 1876-77 term, when his classes were moved to Room 30 of the new Woodburn Hall, completed in 1876. In compiling his portion of Maury's Centennial volume of the *Resources of West Virginia* (1876), he listed sixty-nine trees and sixteen shrubs.

Israel C. White (Fig. 24) was born November 1, 1848, near Wadestown, in Monongalia County, Virginia. He attended West Virginia University, receiving the bachelor of arts degree in 1872 and the master of arts degree in 1875. In 1877, he received the master of arts degree from Columbia University, and his doctor of philosophy degree from the University of Arkansas in 1880.

Fig. 2. West Virginia University in 1883 (From a sketch in the University catalog for 1883-84.)

From 1877 to 1881, Professor White continued the same courses in botany that had been given by Professor Fontaine for the past several years. In 1881-82 his title was changed to Professor of Geology and Natural History. The Agricultural Department continued on a two-year basis, with the course of botany and vegetable physiology being given in the third term of the freshman year, but the curriculum of the Scientific Department was expanded to four years, and botany was offered in the third term of the sophomore year. During the remaining tenure of Dr. White, the same botany courses were offered and Gray's *School and Field Book,* and Bessey's *Structural Botany* were the basic textbooks. There were eleven students enrolled in botany in 1883-84, thirty-five in 1885-86, and thirty-seven in 1886-87.

In 1887-88 Professor White was made professor of geology and **James William Hartigan,** M. D., became professor of anatomy, physiology and hygiene, and natural history. Field botany continued to be given by Dr. White during the spring term, and structural botany was given by Dr. Hartigan in the fall and winter terms. He stated, "The general anatomy and physiology of plants will first be studied, and then the special anatomy and physiology of plant tissue, together with the microscopical examination of these, and practical work in bacteriology." Textbooks and reference books used were Bessey's *Structural Botany,* Gray, Sachs, Bentley, Cooke, Crookshank's *Bacteriology,* and Dawson's *Geological History of Plants.* Dr. White was not associated with the teaching of botany after the 1889-90 term, and resigned from the University in 1892 to take charge of a petroleum business.

Dr. Hartigan was born in Lexington, Virginia, April 19, 1863. He received the M. D. degree in 1884 at the College of Wooster, at Bellevue Hospital Medical College in 1887, at Baltimore Medical College in 1887, and at Indiana College for Eclectic Medicine in 1888, and the master of arts degree from West Virginia University in 1888. After joining the staff of the University in 1887, he was made professor of biology in 1888-89, and was appointed Surgeon of the Corps of Cadets in 1889, and was instructor in physical training and director of the gymnasium in 1891. He continued at the University through the 1898-99 term, teaching botany, in addition to his other duties. He served as a practicing physician for many years and as a member of the State Legislature from 1927-31. He died January 28, 1950.

Although no change was made in the teaching of botany for the 1889-90 term, the year had much significance for botany at the University, because Charles Frederick Millspaugh, M. D., was appointed as botanist and microscopist, on the staff of the Agricultural Experiment Station, and may be thought of as officially the first "Botanist" on the University's staff. His contributions to botany during the three years that he spent at the University were of such prime importance that the following chapter is devoted to him.

During this period when botany was being established at the University, botanical explorations continued to be made by botanists from within as well as from outside the State. Some of the representative contributors follow:

Dr. A. S. Todd, as chairman of a committee of the Medical Society of West Virginia, in 1867 and in 1871 published a list of the "Medicinal Plants of West Virginia," consisting of nine trees, seven shrubs, and sixty herbs.

William Marriott Canby (1831-1904), an extensive botanical collector of Wilmington, Delaware, made a small collection near Grafton in Taylor County in 1868. His specimens are in the herbarium of the New York College of Pharmacy. *Pachistima canbyi* Gray is named for him.

J. H. Diss Debarr, State Commissioner of Immigration, in his "Handbook of West Virginia," in 1870, listed fifty-two species of trees and twelve species of shrubs. It is interesting to note that he designed the West Virginia State Seal.

J. S. Merriam made a collection of plants in the vicinity of Harpers Ferry in Jefferson County in 1871. His specimens were deposited in the U. S. National Herbarium, Washington, D. C.

Joseph Francis James, of Ohio, spent about two weeks in 1877, studying the flora in the region of the Guyandotte and Great Kanawha rivers from Huntington to Kanawha Falls, Hawk's Nest, and Loup Creek, in Fayette County. His specimens were deposited in the Gray Herbarium of Harvard University and in the Farlow Herbarium of Cryptogamic Botany.

E. Richardson collected in the vicinity of Wheeling, Ohio County, in 1877 and 1879, and near Bethany, Brooke County, in 1878. His plants are in the U. S. National Herbarium, Washington, D. C.

Henry Ney Mertz of Wheeling, Steubenville, etc., and **Gustav Guttenberg,** of Wheeling, Erie and Pittsburgh, collected extensively from 1877 to 1888 through the northern counties of the state from Wheeling to Harpers Ferry. In 1878 they manifolded "A check list of the plants of West Virginia," in which they listed 590 species. This list now appears to have been lost, although Millspaugh apparently had it available in the preparation of his own check list (1913) and cites more than 140 collections by Mertz and Guttenberg. Mr. Mertz, in a letter to H. N. Patterson dated January 11, 1879, said: "I have been thinking of having a check list of the plants of West Virginia, so far as I have been able to determine them, printed." In another letter to Mr. Patterson, dated January 10, 1880, he said: "Having moved out of West Va., although I am only across the river from W. Va., I have given up my idea of publishing a catalogue of W. Va. plants. My colaborer, Prof. Guttenberg, has also moved out of W. Va. to Erie, Pa. This leaves W. Va. almost botanist-*less*."

Mr. Mertz was born at Bellaire, Ohio, in 1846 and attended Bethany College in 1868-70. He was the first principal of the Ritchie School in Wheeling, resigning in 1879 to accept the superintendency of the Steubenville, Ohio, schools, a position he held until his retirement in 1901. He died in 1926. (See Charles A. Wingerter, "Greater Wheeling and Vicinity," p. 462. 1912.)

Dr. Guttenberg was born May 10, 1844 at Salzburg, Austria, and spent several years teaching language and science in Erie (1879-81) and Pittsburgh, Pennsylvania (1889-96). He died near Vienna, Austria, June 29, 1896. Only his untimely death, apparently, kept him from being appointed first director of the new Carnegie Museum. West Virginia plant specimens collected by Mertz and Guttenberg are in the herbarium of Carnegie Museum, with a few duplicates in the herbarium of West Virginia University.

H. N. Mertz and **Miss Hattie Jones,** in 1878, made a comprehensive collection of the plants of Cranberry Summit, Preston County. Their specimens are in the herbarium of the Carnegie Museum, Pittsburgh.

Charles Reid Barnes, of the University of Chicago, in 1879 collected along Kanawha River from Charleston to Gauley Bridge. His specimens were placed in the herbarium of Wabash College. (See his "Notes from West Virginia," *Bot. Gaz.* 4:181-182. 1879.)

John Merle Coulter, Professor of Botany, of Wabash College, later of the University of Chicago, in 1879 collected a few interesting plants along the Kanawha River from Charleston to Gauley Bridge. His specimens were deposited in the herbarium of Wabash College.

Captain John Donnell-Smith, of Washington, D. C., spent his summers at Oakland, Maryland, from 1879 to 1882, and made occasional short trips to various points in West Virginia, particularly along the Baltimore and Ohio Railroad from Terra Alta to Grafton and Mannington, and collected plants that appeared to be of special interest. His plants are in the U. S. National Herbarium, Washington, D. C.

Cyrus Guernsey Pringle, a noted botanical collector of Charlotte, Vermont, made a small but interesting collection at White Sulphur Springs and in the vicinity of Ronceverte, in 1880. His specimens are deposited in the herbarium of the University of Vermont.

Thomas Conrad Porter and **John Howard Redfield** collected from White Sulphur Springs to Hawk's Nest in 1880. Professor Porter's specimens were placed in the herbarium of Lafayette College, Easton, Pennsylvania, and those of Dr. Redfield in the herbarium of the Philadelphia Academy of Sciences.

Augustine Dawson Selby, while superintendent of schools at Huntington, collected plants in his vicinity from 1885 to 1887, and extended his plant observations up the Kanawha River as far as Kanawha Falls.

Samuel Boardman Brown, while principal of the Normal School at Glenville, made a large collection of plants in Berkeley and Gilmer counties, from 1885 to 1890. Later he was professor of geology at West Virginia University.

Charles David White, while engaged in paleobotanical studies in connection with his work as geologist of the U. S. Geological Survey, from 1886 to 1894, collected a few plants, principally ferns, which were deposited in the U. S. National Herbarium.

Adolph Koenig, a physician of Pittsburgh, collected about twenty numbers at Wapacomo, "The Rocks," near Romney, Hampshire County, during the summer of 1887. This collection is in the West Virginia University Herbarium, constituting the oldest part of the Herbarium.

Dr. Rosecrans Workman (1861-1905), a physician at Bayard, Grant County, collected a representative series of flowering plants of his neighborhood from 1888 to 1891. This collection was acquired by the West Virginia University Herbarium in 1963, through the courtesy of his grand-nephew, Glenn O. Workman, Jr. (p. 87).

Winfield E. Hill, notes (in *Garden and Forest* 3:182-183, 1890), a few plants from Fairview, Hancock County, observed in 1889.

Merton Benway Waite, pathologist in the Bureau of Plant Industry, U. S. Department of Agriculture, spent about a week in 1889 in Fayette and Greenbrier counties collecting parasitic fungi. He secured about 300 numbers at Kanawha Falls and about 200 at White Sulphur Springs. In 1911 he collected a few numbers of like material in Berkeley County, near Gerrardstown, and Morgan County, at Sleeping Creek, Paw Paw and Hancock. His collection was deposited in the herbarium of the U. S. Bureau of Plant Industry.

REFERENCES

BARTHOLOMEW, ELIZABETH ANN. "Henry Ney Mertz," *Castanea* 28:103-107. 1963.

CORE, EARL L. "The Botanical Exploration of West Virginia," *Proc. W. Va. Acad. Sci.* 10:46-60. 1936.

CORE, EARL L. "Botany at West Virginia University, 1867-1900," *Proc. W. Va. Acad. Sci.* 24:72-78. 1952.

CORE, EARL L. "Outlines of the Flora of West Virginia." Morgantown: West Virginia University Bookstore, 1954.

CORE, EARL L. "Plant Life of West Virginia." New York: Scholar's Library, 1960.

MILLSPAUGH, C. F. "Botanical Field Work in the State." Pages 2-13 in West Virginia Geological Survey 5(A). Wheeling: Wheeling News Litho. Company, 1913.

RODGERS, A. D., III. "John Merle Coulter: Missionary in Science." Princeton: Princeton Univ. Press. 1944.

CHAPTER III

The Shale Barrens

Early in the history of West Virginia, regions of unusual botanical interest and extensive exploration were the amazing *shale barrens*, with their remarkable endemic flora. This narrow strip of shale of Ordovician and Devonian age outcrops in the mid-Appalachian region along both sides of the Virginia-West Virginia border, extending northward across western Maryland into central Pennsylvania.

In 1911, Edward S. Steele[1] coined the term "shale-barren" to designate this peculiar type of plant habitat. Steele states:

> "This land is made up of exposures of shale in different stages of disintegration, these at the point chiefly investigated consisting of the Romney formation of the Lower Devonian.[2] In the valleys these are reduced to clay, originally covered with good forest, and when cleared susceptible of tillage. But the declivities and uplands bear at most a low and open growth of oak and pine or frequently a still lower growth of scrub oak, kalmia, and other shrubs, in either case with an admixture of herbaceous plants. The formations are so open that over large areas they can be penetrated on foot with no great difficulty. The barrenness is perhaps largely due to the constant washing away of the finer particles of soil, but in some cases it seems as if it must be chargeable to chemical composition. The plant covering, I should say, is mildly xerophytic, but there is no evidence of extreme drought. On the contrary, the vegetation here maintains itself through the season even on sunbeaten slopes as well as that on other soils similarly situated. The variety of plant life is very considerable and together with many plants well known on other substrata, these barrens possess a number of species peculiar to themselves."

[1]"New or Noteworthy Plants from the Eastern United States." *Contr. U. S. Nat'l. Herb.* 13:359-374. 1911.

[2]Classified as Middle Devonian by the West Virginia Geological Survey.

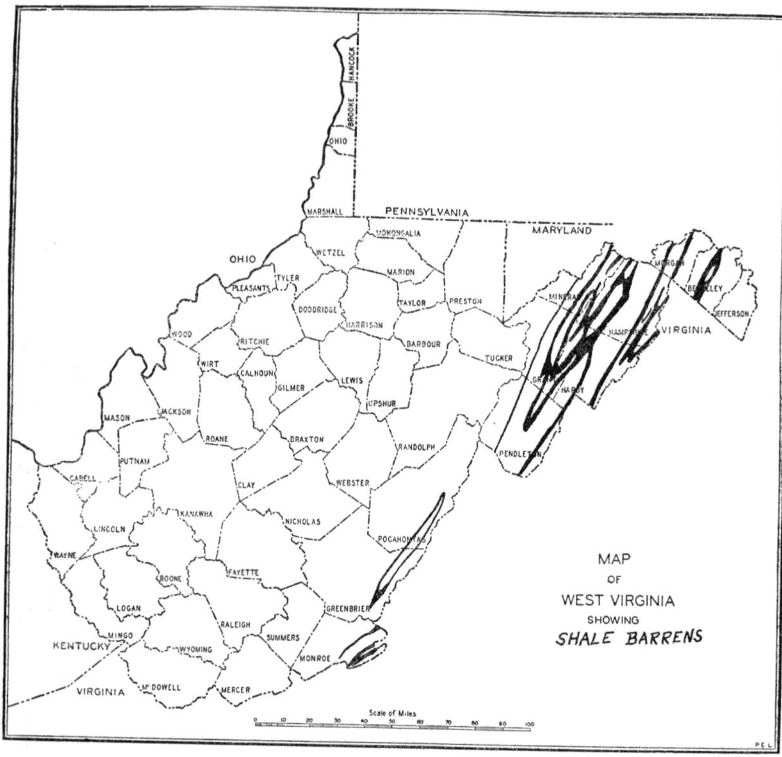

Fig. 3. Map showing a general range of shale barrens in West Virginia.

Describing a shale barren in Virginia, Steele characterized it as "one of the most fascinating spots in which it has been my fortune to botanize."[3]

Edgar T. Wherry, who has been the principal student of the shale-barren flora, states:[4]

> "These barrens are developed on shale-slopes—places where hard shaly rocks of the Romney (Middle Devonian) and Jennings (early Upper Devonian) formations outcrop on steep hillsides, the surface being strewn with frost-broken fragments. They are typically occupied by a sparse, scrubby growth of pine, oak, mountain-laurel, and other woody plants, wherever conditions permit the accumulation of sufficient soil . . . The peculiarities of the

[3]*Op. cit.*, p. 360.

[4]"Plants of the Appalachian Shale Barrens," *Jour. Wash. Acad. Sci.* 20:43-52. 1930.

shale-slopes which lead to their being occupied by endemic plants appear to be the sparsity of soil, the way in which the loose rock-flakes creep down the slopes under the influence of weather, and the limited amount of available moisture and nutrient elements. The rock is made up largely of quartz and clay minerals, and exhibits a neutral reaction."

Although several shale-barren areas are found in West Virginia the classic shale-barren is located at White Sulphur Springs on Kate's Mountain. The early investigation of the flora of this area by persons with botanical training from outside the state was due largely to three factors: the completion of the Chesapeake and Ohio Railroad through the area in 1873, the early development of White Sulphur Springs as a world-famous resort, and the establishment of the New York Botanical Garden in 1896, with Nathaniel Lord Britton as its first director. Britton and Judge Addison Brown, authors of the "Illustrated Flora" (1898), vacationed there and also members of the Garden staff and many amateur botanists came there to collect plants. The vicinity of White Sulphur Springs is the type location for at least eight of the shale-barren endemics, including Yellow Buckwheat (*Eriogonum alleni* Watson), White-haired leatherflower (*Clematis albicoma* Wherry), Kate's Mountain Clover (*Trifolium virginicum* Small), Large-flowered Evening Primrose (*Oenothera argillicola* Mack.), Mountain Pimpernel (*Pseudotaenidia montana* Mack.), Sword-leaf Phlox (*Phlox buckleyi* Wherry), Moss-pink (*Phlox brittonii* Small), and Everlasting Groundsel (*Senecio antennariifolius* Britton).

Phlox buckleyi was originally collected by S. B. Buckley in June, 1838, at White Sulphur Springs, but remained unnamed for nearly a century. It was named by Wherry in 1930. Dr. Wherry notes that, although not growing on barrens, it seems to thrive best in woods near the bases of shale-slopes.[5] The plant is known in West Virginia only in two other counties, Pocahontas and Summers. *Clematis albicoma,* so far as recorded, was first collected by Gustav Guttenberg on Kate's Mountain, July 31, 1877, and was named and described by Wherry in 1931.[6] *Eriogonum alleni* was first collected by Timothy Field Allen (1837-1902), of New York, in the vicinity of White Sulphur Springs and named by Sereno Watson.[7] *Trifolium virginicum*

[5]*Jour. Wash. Acad. Sci.* 20:49. 1930.
[6]*Jour. Wash. Acad. Sci.* 21:198. 1931.
[7]*Gray's Manual,* 6th ed., p. 734. 1889.

was discovered in 1892 by John Kunkel Small, a member of the staff of the New York Botanical Garden.[8] The type specimen of *Senecio antennariifolius* was collected May 16, 1897, by T. F. Allen and N. L. Britton, near White Sulphur Springs.[9] The type specimen of *Phlox brittonii* was collected by N. L. Britton at White Sulphur Springs in May, 1898, and named for him by Small.[10] Kenneth Kent Mackenzie (1877-1934), an attorney and amateur botanist of New York, discovered *Oenothera argillicola* at White Sulphur Springs, August 23, 1903,[11] and *Pseudotaenidia montana* on August 29, 1903, on Kate's Mountain.[12] On this trip he collected in the vicinity of White Sulphur Springs from August 27 to September 9, collecting a total of 187 numbers of interesting plants, which were deposited in the New York Botanical Garden Herbarium. Some of his publications of interest to West Virginia botanists include the following:

"A new genus of North American Umbelliferae: *Pseudotaenidia.*" *Torreya* 3:158-159. 1903.

"Notes on the evening primroses." *Torreya* 4:56-57. 1904.

"Notes on Carex IV." *Bull Torr. Bot. Club* 35:261-270. 1908.

"Notes on Carex VI." *Bull. Torr. Bot. Club* 37:231-250. 1910.

"Notes on Carex IX." *Bull. Torr. Bot. Club* 42:603-621. 1915.

"Carex brevior." *Am. Midl. Nat.* 4: September, 1915.

"Notes on *Carex* X." *Bull. Torr. Bot. Club* 43:423-434. 1916.

"Notes on *Carex* XIII." *Bull. Torr. Bot. Club* 50:343-358. 1923.

"Cariceae." *In. North American Flora* 18:1-478. 1931-35.

"North American Cariceae." N. Y. Bot. Garden. 2 vols. 1940.

Other barrens near Sweet Springs, Monroe County, once a resort area, have been much studied. Most of the familiar barren plants are found here, and the type locality for Velvet Bindweed (*Convolvulus purshianus* Wherry) is found here.[13] Pursh visited this region in 1805. *Allium oxyphilum* Wherry has its type locality at Lillydale, also in Monroe County[14]

At numerous places in Hampshire County, and especially near Hanging Rock shale-barren plants occur. Shale-barren Pussytoes (*Antennaria virginica* Stebbins) was discovered here.

[8]*Mem. Torr. Bot. Club* 4:112. 1894.
[9]Britton and Brown, "Illus. Fl." ed. 1. Vol. 3, p. 478. 1898.
[10]*Bull. Torr. Bot. Club* 27:279. 1900.
[11]*Torreya* 4:56, 57. 1904.
[12]*Torreya* 3:158, 159. 1903.
[13]*Proc. Pa. Acad. Sci.* 7:163. 1933.
[14]*Jour. Wash. Acad. Sci.* 15:370-372. 1925.

Dr. G. L. Stebbins' visit to the area on May 2, 1933, resulted in the announcement of this new species growing chiefly but not exclusively on the barrens.[15]

It seems fitting in connection with the discussion of shale barrens to give short biographies of the following well-known botanists who have contributed so much to botany in general and to a more limited degree to the development of botany in West Virginia.

Nathaniel Lord Britton, an outstanding systematic botanist, an authority on the American flora, was born at Staten Island, N. Y., on January 15, 1859. He graduated in 1879 from Columbia University, and in 1881 he received the degree of doctor of philosophy from the same institution. After serving as instructor in geology from 1879 to 1887 and as instructor and adjunct professor of botany from 1886 to 1891, he was made professor and head of the department of botany at Columbia University, serving in this capacity until 1896. In 1896 he became director-in-chief of the New York Botanical Garden, which was created as the result of his efforts, and which under his guidance became one of the leading institutions for the advancement of botany. He served as director until his retirement in 1929.

Dr. Britton specialized in the flora of North America, and in the flora of the West Indies, Bolivia and Paraguay. He is perhaps best known as the author of "Illustrated Flora of the Northern United States and Canada," with Addison Brown (1896-98; 2nd ed., 1913). It is interesting to note that he was author of "The Bahama Flora," with C. F. Millspaugh (1920). He wrote numerous botanical papers, and edited the *Bulletin of the Torrey Botanical Club,* 1888-97. He helped organize the Botanical Society of America and was its president in 1898 and 1920. He died in New York, June 25, 1934.

John Kunkel Small (1869-1938) was born at Harrisburg, Pa., on January 31, 1869. He received his bachelor of arts degree from Franklin and Marshall College in 1892 and the degree of doctor of science in 1912. He received the degree of doctor of philosophy from Columbia University in 1895. He was curator of the Herbarium at Columbia from 1895 to 1898 and when the herbarium was moved to the newly established New York Botanical Garden, he accompanied it as curator of museums and herbarium. He served in this position until 1906,

[15]*Rhodora* 37:229-237. 1935.

and from 1907 to 1932 was head curator at the Garden, becoming chief research curator in 1932.

Dr. Small was a member of the American Association for the Advancement of Science and of the Torrey Botanical Club.

He was mainly interested in the flora of the southern United States, and wrote three guides to its study, the last of which, his "Manual of the Southeastern Flora," published in 1933, is the standard manual for the region.

An exploring trip of a week's duration in July, 1892 into White Sulphur Springs resulted in the discovery of several species of plants new to science, including *Trifolium virginicum*, the famous Kate's Mountain Clover.

Edgar T. Wherry, son of Albert C. and Elizabeth (Doll) Wherry, was born at Philadelphia, Pennsylvania, September 10, 1885. After attending Friends Central School in Philadelphia in 1899-1902, he attended the University of Pennsylvania, receiving the bachelor of science degree in chemistry in 1906, and the doctor of philosophy degree in mineralogy in 1909. He was a research student at the University of Heidelberg, Germany, in 1910.

Dr. Wherry served as instructor and assistant professor at Lehigh University in 1908-1913; assistant curator, United States National Museum in 1913-1917; crystallographer to principal chemist, United States Department of Agriculture in 1917-30; and in the Department of Botany of the University of Pennsylvania, as associate professor in 1930-41, professor in 1941-1955, and emeritus professor since 1955.

He is a member of the Mineralogical and Geological Society of America, Ecological Society of America, American Fern Society, American Rock Garden Society, American Association for the Advancement of Science, Southern Appalachian Botanical Club, and many other organizations.

Dr. Wherry has made remarkably comprehensive and discriminating studies of the flora of the mountain-region, especially of the shale barrens and certain plant families. He has contributed about 100 specimens to the United States National Herbarium, 2000 specimens to the Herbarium of the Academy of Natural Sciences of Philadelphia, and 5000 specimens to the University of Pennsylvania Herbarium. Many duplicates of his collections are in the Herbarium of West Virginia University.

Dr. Wherry has written the following books: "Wild Flower Guide" (1948), "Guide to Eastern Ferns" (1937; 2nd ed., 1942), "The Genus *Phlox*" (1955). He has also written several hundred articles, all indexed in such places as *Chemical Abstracts* and *Biological Abstracts*. Some of his articles relevant to West Virginia include the following: "A long lost phlox." *Jour. Wash. Acad. Sci.* 20:25-28. 1930; "Plants of the Appalachian shale barrens." *Jour. Wash. Acad. Sci.* 20:43-52. 1930; "*Heuchera hispida* Pursh rediscovered." *Rhodora* 35:118-119. 1933; "Notes on *Asarum* in West Virginia." *Castanea* 1:23-24. 1936; "Polemoniaceae of the Middle Appalachian region." *Castanea* 1:13-15, 32-35. 1936; "A northern fern in West Virginia." *Amer. Fern Jour.* 28:123. 1938; "Recent fern finds in West Virginia." *Castanea* 4:1-4. 1939; "Shale barren plants on other geological formations." *Castanea* 18:64-65. 1953; and, with Fred W. Gray, "The West Virginia locality of the southeastern relative of *Woodsia scopulina*." *Amer. Fern Jour.* 16:92-95. 1926.

REFERENCES

CORE, EARL L. "The Botanical Exploration of West Virginia," *Proc. W. Va. Acad. Sci.* 10:46-50. 1936.

CORE, EARL L. "John Kunkel Small." *Castanea* 3:27, 28. 1938.

CORE, EARL L. "The Shale Barren Flora of West Virginia," *Proc. W. Va. Acad. Sci.* 14:27-36. 1940.

CORE, EARL L. "Ranges of Some Plants of the Appalachian Shale Barrens," *Castanea* 17:105-116. 1952.

CORE, EARL L. "Outlines of the Flora of West Virginia." Morgantown: West Virginia University Bookstore, 1954.

CORE, EARL L. "Plant Life of West Virginia." New York: Scholar's Library, 1960.

HUMPHREY, H. B. "Makers of North American Botany." Ronald Press, New York. 1961. (Articles on Allen, Britton, and Small.)

MILLSPAUGH, C. F. *Botanical Field Work in the State.* Pages 2-13 in West Virginia Geological Survey 5(A). Wheeling: Wheeling News Litho. Company, 1913.

"Nathaniel Lord Britton," *Encyclopaedia Britannica* (1960 ed.), IV, 205.

CHAPTER IV

Charles Frederick Millspaugh

Charles Frederick Millspaugh (1854-1923), the first "Father"[1] of West Virginia botany, was born in Ithaca, New York, the son of John Hill and Marion (Cornell) Millspaugh. As a young man he developed a strong interest in the outdoors. While Louis Agassiz was on a fishing trip near Ithaca the two naturalists became acquainted, and the chance meeting developed into a lasting friendship. He was a nephew of Ezra Cornell, founder of Cornell University, where he was a student during the years 1872-75. He later attended the New York Homoeopathic Medical College and received the doctor of medicine degree in 1881. During the next nine years he practiced medicine in Binghamton, New York, but became increasingly interested in plants, publishing from 1884 to 1887 a work "American Medicinal Plants," in six parts, with 180 full-page color plates prepared by himself.

Dr. Millspaugh came to West Virginia University in the summer of 1889, when the University was, as he said, located "on one of the main roads leading into Morgantown."[2] As a member of the staff of the State Experiment Station his official title was botanist and microscopist and his work was entirely in the field of research.

Before 1889 only a few fragmentary investigations had been conducted into the flora of West Virginia, largely by "a few transient botanists who have worked over, for their own personal pleasure, the neighborhood of some vacation resort."[3]

Dr. Millspaugh was forced immediately to the conclusion that the prime requisite was a "full knowledge of what species of vegetation might be found in this state; where each species best grew, and what were its characteristics in the localities naturally chosen. To a thorough knowledge of this point, three special duties devolved upon me: first, to travel and observe,

[1]Earl L. Core, "Plant Life of West Virginia." New York: Scholar's Library, 1960. p. 4.
[2]*W. Va. Agr. Exp. Sta. Rept.* 3:103. 1891.
[3]*W. Va. Agr. Exp. Sta. Bull.* 24:315. 1892.

Fig. 4. Charles Frederick Millspaugh

meantime taking copious notes; second, to obtain specimens of each species of herb, shrub, or tree, and preserve the same for future reference at the station; and third, to note by the natural inhabitants of the soil what cultivated plants might best succeed in the various sections of the state. It will readily be seen by this that the work laid out for this department for the first year was purely of a foundational type, tending toward a knowledge of the vegetable and soil resources of the State."[4]

[4]*W. Va. Agr. Exp. Sta. Rept.* 3:89. 1891.

The winter of 1889-90 was spent largely in getting together the necessary apparatus and materials and laying plans for the work of the next season. He was an excellent photographer and "fitted up a photographic developing room with every convenience for work, obtaining a camera with lenses, together with all the necessary chemicals and apparatus for developing, printing, and toning the pictures taken . . . Thus fitted out, I have taken this season a large number of negatives of such views, objects, and things as I desired in my own department, or other members of the staff wished to preserve in theirs."[5] His keen interest in photography led to the publication of a highly detailed and well-illustrated paper entitled, "Photography: Its Application to Station Work,"[6] giving a full account of the complete outfit and method of using it. Several plates illustrating the Third Annual Report of the Experiment Station are from his photographs.

By the end of this period he found the microscopic "section of the Station . . . well equipped with all the accessories for scientific work upon minute forms of life and matter," although "so far I have had time only to measure and tabulate the eyepieces and lenses, arrange the apparatus for whatever work may fall to me in aiding other departments . . . and mounting several results of experiments."[7]

"On the 16th of April, 1890, we received in excellent condition from the Department of Agriculture at Washington, thirteen bundles of cuttings of Austrian Basket Osiers for the purpose of experimentation, to determine whether this locality was or was not suitable to their growth for the purpose of willow-ware manufacture."[8] These were planted in a plot on the University Campus.

With the advent of spring he was ready to undertake his botanical survey of the state. "In entering upon botanical investigation in this state, I found the field almost a virgin one, so nearly so indeed that I deemed collecting an important branch of the primary work in this department, and therefore began immediately the task of placing in my laboratory a typical specimen of each tree, shrub, and herb in the state."[9]

"Beginning the first of April, trips about Monongalia County

[5]*Ibid.* 3:102.
[6]*Ibid.* 3:122-144.
[7]*Ibid.* 3:101.
[8]*Ibid.* 3:113.
[9]*Ibid.* 3:90.

were made, for the purpose of observation and collection of specimens upon the plan usually adopted in explorations of this kind, and a list of the species collected was begun under arbitrary numbers, and continued from this date until the period of late frosts. So much time was spent in this county on account of its nearness to the laboratory. In collecting, everything met with was taken when found in typical condition, special care being employed in searching for natural grasses, forage plants, weeds, and medicinal herbs. In connection with this work as conducted in Monongalia County, two trips of more extensive nature were made as follows:

"In company with the Station entomologist,[10] I began at noon on the second of July, a trip by team and wagon, from Parkersburg on the Ohio, east to the valley of Tygart's River in Randolph County, thence south-west to the Gauley River, westerly along the Great Kanawha River to Charleston, and north to the starting point. This trip covered 376 miles of road, led us through twelve counties, and consumed 27 days.

"Our route in Wood County led along the south bank of the Little Kanawha River to the county line beyond Leachtown. Here 68 species not before met with this season were added to the collection, and many valuable notes were taken for future reference. Entering Wirt County still upon the south bank of the river, we proceeded to Elizabeth, where the north bank was gained, which we kept substantially to Glenville, the county seat of Gilmer. In Wirt 45 species were added, and in Calhoun 16 more. Leaving Glenville by the principal pike, we passed up Leading Creek, a tributary to the Little Kanawha, crossing a dividing ridge to a small tributary of the Monongahela, along which our route led to Weston, the county seat of Lewis. Here our first Sunday was spent in rest, and our route continued the following day, along another tributary[11] to the same river, across another divide to a branch of the Buckhannon River, thence to Buckhannon, the county seat of Upshur. The similarity of the flora of the counties so far crossed, give me but three additional species in Gilmer and eleven in Lewis counties, though my notes increased in value and number.

"From Buckhannon our route upon the famous Staunton Pike now led us away from the courses of streams, and by easy grades to the deep gap in Rich Mountain which formed one of

[10]A. D. Hopkins.
[11]Stonecoal Creek.

the earliest fields of battle during the war. From here, a side trip afoot to Lone Sugar Knob was made; after which we proceeded down the mountain to Beverly, the county seat of Randolph. One day was lost at Beverly on account of sickness, and the following two occupied in leisurely ascending Tygart's Valley River through its broad bottom and rugged road for 10 miles to the summit of Point Mountain, where our second Sunday was spent. Upshur County yielded me 40 species—many of which were of great interest, and the trip along the valley and over the mountain in Randolph 108 more.

"Here upon Point Mountain at an elevation of 3,700 feet above the sea level lie the most wonderful hardwood forests it was ever my pleasure to visit, the majestic specimens of cherry (*Prunus serotina*) rising 60 feet without a limb, and full 60 more in foliage, while the 'poplar' (*Liriodendron tulipifera*) here attains great size. The oaks of different species (*Quercus rubra* and *nigra*[12]), magnolias (*Magnolia acuminata, umbrella,*[13] and *fraseri*), maples (*Acer saccharinum,*[14] Marsh., not L., and its variety *nigra*) and chestnut (*Castanea vesca,* var. *americana*[15]) form forests of thousands of acres, in which, strange to say, at this altitude and distance from water, there is a large amount of black walnut (*Juglans nigra*). It was along the road through this great forest for a number of miles after leaving the summit, and proceeding toward Addison[16] that great quantities of curled maple attracted my attention where the foresters had cut down the trees along the road that the sun's rays might reach it and dry its almost impassable ruts.

"Upon the highest pinnacle of Point Mountain, I saw the first growth of Canada thistle I have met with since my residence in this state. It grew where, should the seeds have developed, they might readily have been blown by the slightest wind into three counties. This growth I took care to thoroughly destroy before leaving the spot. The seed from which it grew was probably brought there with that of some grain, as the field in which it stood showed evidence of stubble two years old. Had we accomplished nothing further during this whole trip than to identify and destroy this one patch of that vilest of weeds, its cost in time and money would be repaid many fold.

[12]*Q. velutina.*
[13]*M. tripetala.*
[14]*A. saccharum.*
[15]*C. dentata*
[16]Webster Springs is the post office name.

"From Point Mountain our route lay along the ridge of Buffalo Bull range, through a continuation of the forest mentioned, and then down a romantic but somewhat perilous mountain road, for ten miles, into Addison, the county seat of Webster. We had passed through Valley Head, from the headwaters of the Monongahela system of rivers to that of the Great Elk. Addison, looking flat enough upon our map, was found to be deep in the mountain vastness, from which next day we were extricated by making an ascent of 700 feet in less than a mile of road.

"The next point of interest upon the route was the Glade Region between the headwaters of the Elk and Gauley rivers. These glades having an altitude of 2,350 feet are evidently the beds of ancient sphagnum ponds, which have now however lost their waters, leaving only ditches mostly deepened by attempts to reclaim the land. In one of these glades, 'Long Glades,' there still remains about 100 acres of marshy tract, in which cranberries still grow in sufficient quantity to enable one person to pick 2 to 4 bushels per diem during the season. 'Upper,' 'Middle,' 'Welch,' and 'Long Glades' yield 56 species new to my collection, though visited too late in the season to see them in their best floral condition.

"Passing from here into Nicholas County we strike Peter and Elk Creeks tributary to the Gauley River, and follow the windings of the latter through grand forests of hardwood, in which the hemlock becomes for the first time plentiful and the Sweet Gum (*Liquidambar styraciflua*), which continued as far as Jackson County, is first met in the state. Reaching the Gauley we followed its course, skirting the beautiful Gauley Mountains, to its junction on the Great Kanawha; thence along the fertile bottoms of the latter stream, to the city of Charleston, where our third Sunday was spent. On this portion of the trip Nicholas County yielded me twelve and Fayette a like number of interesting species.

"Leaving Charleston on the morning of the 24th of July upon the Charleston, Ripley, and Parkersburg pike, we passed through the Pocatalico country, over the great limestone ridge to Jackson C. H., thence along the fertile hills of that and Wirt counties, to our starting point. Kanawha yielded me 24, and Jackson 17 further species.

"This trip, while placing a diversified collection of 412 species among those already in the Station herbarium, gave me a knowledge of this portion of the state that will assist me materially in all the work falling to my department.

"While in the neighborhood of this great forest range upon the trip just related, we learned that the valuable forests of spruce there were being destroyed by some insect or disease, the extension of which was reported to threaten their utter ruin. Placing this matter before the director of the Station upon our return, we were bade make a special trip to these forests, for the purpose of determining, if possible, the cause, and find a remedy should one suggest itself to us. Accordingly on the 25th of August we left Morgantown by the B. & O. R. R. for Piedmont, where we changed to the West Virginia Central; which carried us over 80 miles through wild mountain forests to Elkins, near the county seat of Randolph, where we arrived late in the evening. Having decided to advance as far as possible southward along the Cheat range, we took the stage for Huttonsville the next afternoon. Although I had already worked over the 21 miles to this point upon our previous trip, through the kindness of the obliging driver who made several halts for the purpose, I was enabled to add quite a number of new specimens to my collections. Huttonsville was reached at 6:30 p. m. in driving rain, which threatened our expedition with delay. The morning of the 27th was so stormy that, with the rains of the previous night, the roads soon became too bad to attempt further progress, and the morning was spent in gaining further particulars concerning the trouble in the forests. Men were sought and found who had been intimately acquainted with the mountain wilds for years, and through their kindness and deep interest in the object of our trip, we gained most of the knowledge that is here represented in figures. Most of these gentlemen had either been surveyors or assistants, hunters or lumbermen, purchasers or buyers' agents, so that the points given were very exact and reliable. To Col. E. Hutton,[17] whose large experience in this region renders him an authority upon the forest, I am under special obligations; not only for figures and facts, but also for kindly hospitality. The afternoon was spent in gathering plants in the neighborhood and gleaning information concerning the weeds of that locality.

"The morning of the 28th opened bright and auspicious, enabling an early start. Our road for miles lay along the broad valley of Tygart's River, and easterly along a tributary stream,

[17]Col. Elihu Hutton (1837-1916), C.S.A., was a great-uncle of Dr. Eugene Hutton (see p. 152).

to the base of the mountain; where the ascent was begun upon the continuation of the old Staunton pike, made so famous through this region first by those bright sketches of Porte Crayon, and later by the Civil War. Traversing the beautiful grades and windings of this road, the flora became more boreal the higher we ascended, until at an elevation of 3,425 feet we reached the 'spruce line' eleven miles from Huttonsville. The entomologist's first view of the dead trees suggested, and his investigations soon after proved, that the cause of the trouble lay entirely within the province of his department; thus leaving me free to the study of living vegetation, the novelty and profusion of which had already deeply interested me. Two miles further we gained the summit of Old White Top, the scene of the battle of Cheat Mountain; from which the view spread before us, first in clear, then hazy distances, of rugged and densely wooded mountain spurs and ranges. As far as the eye could distinguish to the east and south, the deep olive green of the spruce, here and there dotted with the early changing foliage of the cherry, clothed the earth. On turning, however, in our seats, what a change! The vast forests of desolation, extending their bare arms as if in grim mockery from their ruined neighbors, toward their rich leafy brothers, across the black water of Cheat.

"From this summit, 3,650 feet above the sea level, the road drops at a heavy grade down to the river, which has an altitude at this point of 3,310 feet, and is about 2,500 feet above its mouth in southwestern Pennsylvania. Crossing the bridge our stage draws up to the entrance of the only hotel, which, with the postoffice and lumber camp, constitutes the village of Winchester."[18]

At the close of this season, Millspaugh states[19] that "from my present knowledge of the topography of the state, and its character of soil, I estimate that we should have at least of:

Flowering plants	1650 species
Ferns, club mosses, etc.	60 species
Mosses, liverworts, etc.	300 species
Fungi, lichens, etc.	2000 species
Minor forms of vegetable life	100 species
Total	4110 species

[18]*Ibid.* 3:93-97; Winchester is now known as Cheatbridge.
[19]*Ibid.* 3:91.

Although he was keenly interested in taxonomic work, he always kept in mind that he was a member of the staff of the Agricultural Experiment Station and that his first duty was to the farmers of the state. For example, in regard to grasses he wrote: "It is our design to have chemical analyses carefully made at this Station of each and every natural grass and forage plant, to determine their nutritive value, and, after this, to analyze the most nutritious species, to determine the character of soil best suited to their full and characteristic growth."[20]

Also he was especially interested in weeds and in December, 1890 issued the following "Appeal to Farmers:" "It is my intention to issue during the coming season a complete account of the weeds of this state. To do so intelligently and honestly, I need the help of every West Virginia agriculturist who reads this article. I am only one man and cannot conscientiously cover the whole state. I therefore ask you, for the benefit of your farms, to assist me by answering the questions here asked, and mailing your answer to the West Virginia Agricultural Experiment Station, Morgantown, W. Va."[21]

He planned to establish an Arboretum on the Campus. He wrote: "It is my intention to transplant into the University Campus as rapidly as possible, either direct or from raised seedlings, a typical individual of each and every tree and shrub found native in this State; to form an Arboretum in which the agricultural students, Station staff, and the agriculturists of the state may examine under their proper names the useful, ornamental, and detrimental large plants of West Virginia."[22] In the Third Annual Report he presents the following summary:[23]

	Now in Arboretum	To be planted	Total
Native trees	27	48	75
Native shrubs	8	49	57
Cultivated trees	11		11
Cultivated shrubs	14		14
Total	60	97	157

In June, 1891, he wrote: "The work in the botanical department during the past year, with few exceptions, has been confined to systematic botany and the question of the weeds of the state, as I have not been supplied with the necessary literature

[20] *Ibid.* 3:117.
[21] *Ibid.* 3:120; also in *W. Va. Agr. Exp. Sta. Bull.* 12. 1890.
[22] *W. Va. Agr. Exp. Sta. Rept.* 3:102. 1890.
[23] *Ibid.* 3:112.

and apparatus for working out original investigations upon plant diseases, which, however, will be done during the present season. When having, as this report will show, worked out the principal problems for the state in systematic botany, the matter of original investigations upon diseases or crops will constitute the object of this department.

"I have finished and submitted 150 pages of manuscript, comprising a preliminary catalogue of the flora of this state, which contains the notes of species observed as well as a compilation of all the work of others, as far as I could determine in this region . . . The preparatory work necessary to obtain the facts recorded in this catalogue comprises: 63 days spent in the field; 1840 miles of travel by rail; 376 miles by wagon; 37 miles on horseback, and 264 miles on foot. Besides the notes gathered for practical use in the laboratory, I have collected, mounted, and preserved over 1200 specimens, and placed them in shape for reference and exhibit toward explanation in person to farmers and others desiring information upon the vegetation of the state."[24]

"In connection with this work I had the pleasure of discovering a peculiar blackberry in Randolph Co., one not only new to botany and horticulture, but growing entirely without thorns. I hope to make another trip to its locality next season and procure a quantity for the purpose of cultivation at the Station, as the plant bids fair to develop a new and valuable fruit."[25] This blackberry was described by Britton under the name *Rubus millspaughii.*[26]

"Contemporary with this work, I have devoted much time to the study of our weed growths, and have also filed, tabulated, and answered over 300 communications upon weeds received from our farmers, most of which were called forth by my remark in Bulletin 12, issued December last. The results practical and historical of this work will appear in four bulletins . . . as follows:

Your Weeds and Your Neighbor's

Part 1. Weeds as fertilizers
Part 2. Descriptive list of weeds
Part 3. Distribution and bad points of weeds
Part 4. General treatment of weedy fields."[27]

[24]*W. Va. Agr. Exp. Sta. Rept.* 4:41, 42. 1891.
[25]*Ibid.* 4:42.
[26]*Bull. Torr. Bot. Club* 18:366. 1891; see also *Agr. Sci.* 6:66, for a horticultural treatment of the new blackberry.
[27]*W. Va. Agr. Exp. Sta. Rept.* 4:42, 43. 1891.

This material later appeared as bulletins of the Agricultural Experiment Station as follows: Part 1 as Bulletin 19; Part 2 as Bulletin 23; Part 3 as Bulletin 22; and Part 4 never was published. Bulletin 23 is an excellent work of 95 pages, with descriptions of 200 weeds, well illustrated, with references to the medicinal value of various weeds. Commenting on these contributions B. D. Halsted says "The farmers of West Virginia are fortunate in having such a thorough work upon their weeds placed within easy reach of all."[28]

Millspaugh also stated: "The experiment with Austrian Basket Osiers . . . has me with quite a serious set-back on account of the ruthless pulling up of over 80 of the rooting cuttings by some vandal. Nevertheless, from the general condition of those remaining, I feel quite certain that we can not expect to successfully grow basket willows within our borders."[29]

"In the microscopical department I have been engaged principally in the study of a new bacterial disease of the Locust."[30]

"Since my last report but little has been done toward adding species to the Arboretum."[31]

Actually he had added 15 species to his list of native trees and shrubs with two being new to science, viz., *Rubus millspaughii* Britton, and *Spiraea virginiana* Britton[32] which he collected along the Monongahela River on June 20, 1890, below Morgantown (possibly the present Arboretum area).

He further stated: "In assisting at Farmer's Institutes throughout the state . . . I have spent 29 days away from my laboratory in travel and attendance; have traveled 2102 miles by rail and 16 by wagon, and prepared and delivered 8 lectures upon subjects pertaining to my department." He made "over 150 photographic lantern transparencies."[33]

The summer of 1891, like that of the previous year, was spent in the field. In June he made a trip to the Eastern Panhandle and was in the region of Bayard, Grant County, and Davis, Tucker County, early in July. In August he collected in southern West Virginia, stopping on the 11th for a visit with Lawrence William Nuttall, at Nuttallburg, Fayette County, and

[28]*Bull. Torr. Bot. Club* 19:324. 1892.
[29]*W. Va. Agr. Exp. Sta. Rept.* 4:44. 1891.
[30]*Ibid.* 4:44.
[31]*Ibid.* 4:45.
[32]*Bull. Torr. Bot. Club* 17:314. 1890.
[33]*W. Va. Agr. Exp. Sta. Rept.* 4:47. 1891.

on the 12th collected and observed plants in the Hinton and Alderson area.

Mr. Nuttall was at that time a mine owner at Nuttallburg. He spent much of his spare time in the woods, and from 1890 to 1897 collected about 1000 species of flowering plants in addition to 1400 species of fungi. His manuscript of 700 species was used freely by Millspaugh in the preparation of his preliminary check-list. His private herbarium was presented to the University in 1928 and is now filed in the Herbarium.[34]

"A Preliminary Catalogue of the Flora of West Virginia" was published as Bulletin 24 of the West Virginia Agricultural Experiment Station, dated June, 1892. This publication, of 224 pages, was the first real book on the botany of West Virginia. In presenting this publication Dr. Millspaugh stated: "Although I have worked only two seasons among the plants of the State, as a side issue from my duties at the Experiment Station, I can not feel . . . notwithstanding the assistance of those who have contributed toward this catalogue—that more than a beginning has been made toward a knowledge of the plant life within our boundaries. However, this rich field already makes a good showing even when compared with the almost complete work done by many observers combined, in other states."[35]

His "Summary of the Flora" follows:

	Genera	Species	Varieties	Forms	Total
Anthophyta	504	1189	109	23	1321
Pteridophyta	15	39	4	1	44
Bryophyta	66	107	6		113
Thallophyta	94	164		3	167
Total	679	1499	119	27	1645
Of these, there are native to the State					1452
Foreign					193
Total species, varieties, and forms					1645

The work includes original descriptions of four new species of Cryptogams, as well as a number of new varieties of seed plants.

Dr. Millspaugh's connection with the West Virginia Agricultural Experiment Station was, unfortunately, terminated June

[34]See "Former Student Gives Work to University," by Douglas Miller, in *The West Virginia Agriculturist* for February, 1929. The title is misleading since Nuttall was never a regularly enrolled student at the University. See Chap. V of the present work.

[35]*W. Va. Agr. Exp. Sta. Bull.* 24:518. 1892.

30, 1892. The Board of Regents of West Virginia University, at its meeting in June, 1892 "deemed it advisable to change the policy of the Station in regard to botanical work; it being apparent that the efforts of the Station could be more advantageously directed to horticultural work than at present to continue the botanical work. By direction of the Board, the work under way in botany was finished up, and has been published in bulletin form, leaving it fairly well completed as far as it goes and making a good foundation for the horticultural work which was begun Sept. 15th by the appointment of Mr. F. Wm. Rane as horticulturist to the Experiment Station."[36]

That Dr. Millspaugh's work was fully appreciated by his associates at the Experiment Station is indicated by the following comment by John A. Myers, then director of the Station: "In regard to the botanical work done by the Station, I may say that while we were concentrating our energies upon it, no state in the Union did better, or more extensive work, and it resulted in the publication of a preliminary catalogue of the Flora of West Virginia, which, I believe, is the most comprehensive botanical publication issued by any Station in the country."[37]

He appeared on the program of the Botanical Club at the A.A.A.S. meeting in Rochester, Aug. 18-24, 1892, presenting by title "Some noteworthy features of the botany of West Virginia."[38]

In 1894 Dr. Millspaugh was made curator of botany at the Field Museum of Natural History, Chicago, and remained in this position for the remainder of his active life. His interest in botany in West Virginia remained alive and for the next few years, in collaboration with L. W. Nuttall, he continued an investigation of the flora, adding the knowledge of over 1000 species to the preliminary list and finding many new locations for previously published species. In January, 1896, they published jointly their "Flora of West Virginia."[39] The small edition of the preliminary catalogue having been exhausted within a few months of its issue, and many institutions, libraries, and personal workers being unable to secure copies of the work, it was deemed expedient to include in the new list all the species of

[36] *W. Va. Agr. Exp. Sta. Rept.* 5:14. 1897.

[37] "History of West Virginia Agricultural Experiment Station," in *W. Va. Agr. Exp. Sta. Spec. Bull.* 2:127. 1895.

[38] *Bull. Torr. Bot. Club* 19:324. 1892.

[39] "Flora of West Virginia," by Charles Frederick Millspaugh and Lawrence William Nuttall. *Field Columbian Museum Bot.* ser. 1, No. 2:65-276. 1896.

the first publication. The repeated species appear in small capitals, the additional species new to the flora in black-faced type. As in the preliminary catalogue, the original descriptions of all species that had been described from known West Virginia types were republished in full.

The greatest number of additional species were among the fungi, and it was to their collection and study that Mr. Nuttall had devoted most of his spare time after 1893. "His field of search for forms in this class of plants has been very limited, being almost wholly the immediate neighborhood of his home at Nuttallburg, in Fayette County, on New River. Even this small area has furnished the major part of the 980 fungi of this flora, and continues to present additional forms as well as unique hosts upon every search, no matter how casual the examination or short the time devoted to the trip. Fully two-thirds of the species collected have passed under the critical examination of Mr. J. B. Ellis, whose careful consideration of our numbers has been of incalculable assistance in this work."[40] Thirty-six species of fungi were described in the catalogue for the first time.

The following "Summary of the Flora"[41] is quite significant when compared with that presented in the preliminary catalogue:

	Genera	Species
Fungi, etc.	342	980
Lichens	31	115
Thallophyta, etc.	373	1095
Hepaticae	24	32
Musci	42	90
Sphagnae	1	1
Bryophyta	67	123
Equisetae	1	4
Filicinae	14	40
Ophioglossae	2	7
Lycopodae	1	5
Selaginellae	1	1
Pteridophytes	19	57

[40] *Ibid.* 75.
[41] *Ibid.* 80.

Gymnospermae	7	13
Monocotyledonae	95	268
Dicotyledonae	412	1028
Anthophyta	514	1309

Total number of species, varieties, and forms detected in the state to the date of this flora 2584

In 1913 the last and most pretentious work of Dr. Millspaugh on the flora of West Virginia was published by the West Virginia Geological Survey.[42] "The very exhaustive paper of Dr. Millspaugh which forms Part I of the new volume V(A) of the publications of the West Virginia Geological Survey, constitutes an entire revision of the *West Virginia Flora* prepared and published by Dr. Millspaugh in 1896, as a revision of his first publication of a *Preliminary Catalogue of the Flora of West Virginia*, 1892, published by the West Virginia Agricultural Experiment Station when Dr. Millspaugh was connected with that Institution as botanist during the years 1889-1892. The present paper embodies the results of a much wider and later study not only by Dr. Millspaugh through the works and collections of other authors, but also the results of Dr. John L. Sheldon's (professor of botany, W. Va. University) recent studies communicated freely to Dr. Millspaugh for use in his publication, so that a very large addition to the West Virginia flora is thus made known to the world by this labor of love on the part of Dr. Millspaugh, for which all those interested in the botany of the state will be deeply grateful."[43]

Nearly a thousand new names were added in this list, as shown by the following summary:[44]

	Genera	Species
Fungi, etc.	430	1330
Lichens	39	176
Thallophyta, etc.	469	1506

[42] "The Living Flora of West Virginia." *W. Va. Geol. Surv.* 5 (A): i-xiii, 1-389, 454-487. 1913.

[43] *Ibid.* vi.

[44] *Ibid.* 487.

Hepaticae	48	78
Musci	68	171
Sphagnaceae	2	8
Bryophyta	118	257
Equisetae	1	4
Filices	16	43
Ophioglossaceae	2	7
Lycopodiaceae	1	6
Selaginellaceae	1	2
Pteridophyta	21	62
Gymnospermae	8	15
Monocotyledonae	118	347
Dicotyledonae	476	1224
Anthophyta	602	1586
Total number of species, varieties, and forms detected in the state to the date of the flora		3411

Late in 1919, in an effort to recuperate his physical strength after a serious operation, Millspaugh went to Santa Catalina Island off the coast of California. He invited to his island home his old friend L. W. Nuttall, who had that year retired from his mining business. They made a study of the plants of the Island and laid the foundation for their "Flora of Santa Catalina Island," published jointly in January, 1923. This was Dr. Millspaugh's last published work. He died on September 15, 1923.

E. E. Sherff, of Chicago Normal College, in a brief biographical sketch of Dr. Millspaugh, gives an appraisal of his character and work as follows: "To the younger generation of American botanists Dr. Millspaugh was known mainly by reputation, for, busied with many administrative tasks incident to his work, he often had to forego attendance upon conventions of fellow scientists. A full six feet in stature, of erect carriage and decisive manner, he possessed a strong and positive personality not soon to be forgotten by those who knew him. Accurately to appraise his various qualities and powers as a botanist would be wellnigh impossible, nor would the writer, biased with the warm friendship that comes from an acquaintance and close personal contact during the past twelve years, feel equal to the task.

True it is, however, that Dr. Millspaugh's death marks the departure of an able taxonomic worker and one of America's most brilliant organizers of museum displays."[45]

When Dr. Millspaugh left West Virginia in 1892, his collection of 1580 numbers was left in the Experiment Station. This priceless collection was stored in Oglebay Hall, and on July 1, 1933, when the departments of botany and zoology were merged with the department of plant pathology to form the new department of biology, was incorporated into the general Herbarium in Science Hall, later moved to Brooks Hall. This collection is historically of prime importance, being cited in the check-list of the state's flora and constituting the foundation on which succeeding botanists have built.

A paved automobile road providing access to a portion of the West Virginia University Arboretum was named Millspaugh Lane in 1959 (*Arboretum Newsletter*, Vol. 9, No. 4, Winter 1959-60).

The following is a complete list, so far as known, of the publications of Dr. Millspaugh that deal with West Virginia botany:

Report of Botanical Department. *W. Va. Agri. Exp. Sta. Rept.* 3:89, 90. 1891.

Flora of West Virginia. *Ibid.* 3:90, 91.

Collection, Preparation and Mounting of Specimens. *Ibid.* 3:91-93.

Field Work on the Flora. *Ibid.* 3:93-97.

The Black Spruce. *Ibid.* 3:98-101.

Report of Microscopic Section. *Ibid.* 3:101.

Report of Photographic Section. *Ibid.* 3:101, 102.

Arboretum. *Ibid.* 3:102, 103.

Campus Trees and Shrubs. *Ibid.* 3:104-109.

Native Trees and Shrubs of West Virginia. *Ibid.* 3:110-112.

Experiment with Austrian Osiers. *Ibid.* 3:117.

Analyses of Forage Plants and Weeds. *Ibid.* 3:117.

The Canada Thistle. *Ibid.* 3:118-121, illus. (Also distributed as *W. Va. Agr. Exp. Sta. Bull.* 12:271-274, 1890).

Photography: Its Application to Station Work. *W. Va. Agr. Exp. Sta. Rept.* 3:122-144, illus. 1891.

Report of Botanist and Microscopist for 1891. *W. Va. Exp. Sta. Rept.* 4:41-47. 1897.

[45]*Bot. Gaz.* 77:231. 1924. The article presents a brief biography of Dr. Millspaugh, with a portrait. See also *Bull. N. Y. Bot. Gard.* 24:286. 1923, for a short sketch and appraisal.

Your Weeds and Your Neighbor's. Part 1. Weeds as Fertilizers, *W. Va. Agr. Exp. Sta. Bull.* 19:119-127. 1891.

Your Weeds and Your Neighbor's. Part 2. Distribution of our weeds; bad points of weeds; weeds as fodder for stock; chemical weed exterminators. *W. Va. Agr. Exp. Sta. Bull.* 22:177-212. 1892.

Your Weeds and Your Neighbor's. Part 3. Illustrated Descriptive List of Weeds. *W. Va. Agr. Exp. Sta. Bull.* 23:213-308. 1892.

Preliminary Catalogue of the Flora of West Virginia. *W. Va. Agr. Exp. Sta. Bull.* 24:311-538. 1892.

(With L. W. Nuttall) Flora of West Virginia. *Field Columbian Mus. Bot.* ser. 1, no. 2:65-276. 1896.

(With L. W. Nuttall) New West Virginia Lichens. (New species in *Lecidia, Arthronia,* and *Lecanora* by Nylander and Calkins). *Bot. Gaz.* 22:333, 334. 1896.

The Living Flora of West Virginia. *W. Va. Geol. Surv.* 5 (A): i-xiii, 1-389, 454-487. illus. 1913.

REFERENCES

CORE, EARL L. "Contributions of Charles Frederick Millspaugh to the Botany of West Virginia," *Proc. W. Va. Acad. Sci.* 8:82-93. 1935.

CORE, EARL L. "The Botanical Exploration of West Virginia," *Proc. W. Va. Acad. Sci.* 10:46-60. 1936.

CORE, EARL L. "Outlines of the Flora of West Virginia." Morgantown: West Virginia University Bookstore, 1954.

CORE, EARL L. "Plant Life of West Virginia." New York: Scholar's Library, 1960.

HUMPHREY, H. B. "Makers of North American Botany." Ronald Press, New York, 1961. (Article on Millspaugh).

MILLSPAUGH, C. F. "Botanical Field Work in the State." W. Va. Geol. Surv. 5 (A). Wheeling: Wheeling News Litho. Company, 1913.

CHAPTER V

Lawrence William Nuttall

Lawrence William Nuttall, a second "Father" of West Virginia botany, a pioneer amateur botanist, of Nuttallburg, West Virginia, was born near Philipsburg, Pennsylvania, on September 17, 1857. His father, John Nuttall, was born near Accrington, Lancashire, England, in 1817, and Lawrence was the first of his children to be born in America. He was only distantly related to Thomas Nuttall, one of the foremost botanical explorers of the early nineteenth century. He received his formal education at Perryville Academy, Port Royal, Pennsylvania, where he took great interest in botany, and completed his schooling in 1878. His instructor, recognizing his unusual interest, gave him much attention and took him for walks on weekends.

In 1870 his father bought 800 acres of coal property in Fayette County along New River, later adding more acres to these. When the Chesapeake and Ohio Railroad was completed along New River in 1873 Mr. Nuttall began the operation of the mine. The C. & O. put his name on their time-tables and the first shipments were stencilled "Nuttall," although Mr. Nuttall suggested the name Nuttallburg for the village, and this name was accepted by the Post Office Department.[1]

After finishing his schooling, Lawrence came to Nuttallburg to help his father operate the mine. He served as secretary-treasurer of the company and private secretary to his father. He would complete most of his work at the mine in the mornings, leaving the afternoons free to make botanical explorations and studies in the vicinity.

He was united in marriage to Katherine DuBree, of Philipsburg, Pennsylvania, November 11, 1884, and to this union was born a son, John, and another who died in infancy. This union was a further stimulus to his botanical studies, since his wife was interested in butterflies. Many of his specimens were sent to his old teacher for identification, as well as to higher authori-

[1] "How John Nuttall Developed the Keeney's Creek Section," *Fayetteville (W. Va.) State Sentinel,* February 6, 1952.

ties. Of these authorities, one was J. B. Ellis, of Plainfield, New York, who identified many of his species of fungi. For many years Mr. Nuttall and Mr. Ellis corresponded with each other.

Another of these authorities was Dr. Millspaugh, who visited Mr. Nuttall in 1891. As stated in the preceding chapter, Dr.

Fig. 5. Lawrence William Nuttall

Millspaugh freely used the lists of Mr. Nuttall, and collaborated with him. This association with Dr. Millspaugh in 1891 evidently inspired Mr. Nuttall to still greater efforts and during the period from 1890 to 1897 he collected about 1000 species of flowering plants and hundreds of fungi, with at least 108 species of the fungi being new to science. Four species of lichens were also described as new species.[2]

Among plants named for Mr. Nuttall are *Hypoxylon nuttallii* E. & E., *Helotiella nuttallii* E. & E., *Phyllachora nuttalliana* Fairman, *Lecidea nuttallii* Calk. & Nyl., *Jepsonia neonuttalliana* Millspaugh, and *Anychia nuttallii* Small.

In 1894 when Dr. Millspaugh was made curator of botany at the Field Museum of Natural History in Chicago, he continued to correspond with Mr. Nuttall, and in 1896, they published jointly their "Flora of West Virginia."[3] This work added almost 1000 additions to the list of 1892, and of the 980 species of fungi listed the major portion came from Fayette County.

Mr. Nuttall made an interesting discovery among the seed plants, *Carex fraseri*,[4] which had been collected about 1800 by Matthias Kin in the region of "Deigher walli in der wilternus" (p. 4), but which had rarely been seen again by botanists. He found a large colony at Nuttallburg in Fayette County and sent specimens to the Torrey Botanical Club in New York in 1891, where they were exhibited and considered an interesting discovery.

At about this time Mr. Nuttall became acquainted with the well known botanist, John Kunkel Small, of the New York Botanical Garden, who was spending some of his vacations in West Virginia.[5] Later when Dr. Small became interested in the flora of the southeastern states, the two botanists spent several winters together in Florida, collecting specimens and preparing the data on which Small's "Flora of the Southeastern States" was based in part.

John Nuttall died in 1897 and Lawrence Nuttall and his brother-in-law, Jackson Taylor, became sole managers of the old Nuttall mine. The mine showed no profit for many years

[2]For a list of these species see: Earl L. Core, "Lawrence William Nuttall." *Castanea* 17:159-160. 1952.

[3]"Flora of West Virginia," by Charles Frederick Millspaugh and Lawrence William Nuttall. Field Columbian Museum Bot. ser. 1, no. 2:65-276. 1896. See p. 36.

[4]See Roy B. Clarkson, "Fraser's Sedge, *Cymophyllus fraseri* (Andrews) Mackenzie." *Castanea* 26:129-136. 1961.

[5]See *Mem. Torr. Bot. Club* 4:112. 1894.

and was sold in 1903. In 1892 another brother-in-law, George McGaffey, had joined with some other men in opening the First National Bank of Philipsburg, Pennsylvania, and soon became its president.

In 1907 Mr. Nuttall moved to Philipsburg and became associated in the enterprise, and upon the death of Mr. McGaffey, in 1915, was elected president of the bank and served a number of years as such.

Mr. Nuttall continued to spend a part of his time in the study of wild flowers, the spring and summers in Pennsylvania and the winters in Florida, Tucson, and San Antonio. During this time he supplied Mr. Elam Bartholomew with a number of species in quantity for his "North American Uredinales."

In 1902, while Mr. and Mrs. Nuttall were on a Mediterranean cruise they met Dr. and Mrs. D. B. Purinton, and the two couples became warm friends. During the summer of 1906, at the request of Dr. Purinton, then President of West Virginia University, Mr. Nuttall came to Morgantown to assist in identifying rusts and other fungi for the Agricultural Experiment Station. With his family he spent six weeks in Morgantown, but the work was gratis and he had no formal appointment.[6]

In 1919 Dr. Millspaugh, still at the Field Museum, wrote to Mr. Nuttall concerning a project on the flora of Santa Catalina Island, off the coast of California. This region was largely unknown botanically and Millspaugh suggested that they undertake the investigation of this flora. Mr. Nuttall, who had that year retired, was delighted at the prospect and he and his wife spent about two years there. He and Dr. Millspaugh made a study of the plants and laid the foundation for a book on the flora of the Island, published jointly in 1923.[7] A total of 882 species were described in detail, including many previously undescribed, especially among the fungi. The Nuttalls were impressed with the evenness of the temperature and they returned to Philipsburg with the resolution that they would some day go back to California to live.

In 1927 Mr. and Mrs. Nuttall and their son John and family moved to San Diego to live, with residences near each other. Before leaving the East, Mr. Nuttall donated his large and valuable plant collection to the West Virginia University Herbarium. This collection included thousands of specimens of seed

[6]See Earl L. Core, "Lawrence William Nuttall." *Castanea* 17:163. 1952.
[7]Charles F. Millspaugh and Lawrence William Nuttall, "Flora of Santa Catalina Island," *Field Mus. Nat. Hist. Publ.* 212. 413 p. 1923.

plants and ferns, but was especially valuable for the large collection of fungi, including about 1400 species, with type material of most of the species first found in Fayette County.

For the remainder of his life he maintained his interest in botany, learning new and unusual plants, and meeting botanists of the region. He died in San Diego, October 16, 1933.

Honoring this well-known amateur botanist, the Arboretum Committee of West Virginia University in 1953 named an important nature trail in the Arboretum the "Lawrence William Nuttall Trail." (*Arboretum News*, Vol. 3, No. 4, April, 1953).

REFERENCES

CORE, EARL L. "The Botanical Exploration of West Virginia," *Proc. W. Va. Acad. Sci.* 10:46-60. 1936.

CORE, EARL L. "Lawrence William Nuttall," *Castanea* 17:157-164. 1952.

CORE, EARL L. "Plant Life of West Virginia." New York: Scholar's Library, 1960.

MILLER, DOUGLAS W. "Former Student Gives Work to University," *The West Virginia Agriculturist,* (February, 1929), 9, 24. See footnote, p. 35.

CHAPTER VI

John Lewis Sheldon

John Lewis Sheldon, a third "Father"[1] of West Virginia botany, son of Samuel and Lucy Ann Lewis Sheldon, was born November 10, 1865, in Voluntown, Connecticut. He was a teacher in the Connecticut school system from 1885 to 1890, and was an instructor in the Mt. Hermon school. After receiving the B. S., B. Ped. degree from Ohio Northern University in 1895, he taught in the Connecticut public schools from 1895 to 1897. He taught in the preparatory school of the University of Nebraska in 1898, proceeded with graduate work, and received both the degree of bachelor of science from Nebraska and the master of science degree from Ohio Northern in 1899. During 1899-1900 he taught in the Nebraska State Normal School. From 1900 to 1903 he served as an instructor of botany at the University of Nebraska, continued his graduate work, receiving the degree of master of arts in 1901 and the doctor of philosophy degree in 1903.

He came to West Virginia University in 1903 and served as professor of bacteriology until 1907 when he was made professor of botany and bacteriology. In 1913 he was designated as professor of botany, a position he retained until his retirement in 1919.

After coming to West Virginia, Dr. Sheldon made numerous trips over the State, covering mainly Monongalia, Preston, Greenbrier, Monroe, Pocahontas, Berkeley, Jefferson, Randolph, and all those counties along the Ohio River, studying carefully the plant life and making extensive collections. His field work added a large number of species to the previously known flora of the State, many of which were published in Millspaugh's "Living Flora of West Virginia," in 1913. Although he was especially interested in cryptogams, he added a large collection of vascular plants as well. He was a collaborator of the Bureau of Plant Industry, United States Department of Agriculture, in 1902 and 1903 and again from 1905 to 1922.

He was a member of a number of organizations, including the

[1]Earl L. Core. "Plant Life of West Virginia," New York: Scholar's Library, 1960, p. 4.

American Association for the Advancement of Science, Phytopathological Society, Genetic Association, Sullivant Moss Society, Southern Appalachian Botanical Club, Sigma Xi, Phi Epsilon Phi, and Phi Beta Kappa. It was at his suggestion that the Journal of the Southern Appalachian Botanical Club was named *Castanea,* in memory of the dying chestnut, formerly characteristic of the Southern Appalachian forests.

He married Clara Fleming, of Hopkins, Missouri, in 1907, and they had one son, Earl.

Fig. 6. John Lewis Sheldon

In 1939 an entire issue of *Castanea* (4:69-126) was devoted to the life and writings of Dr. Sheldon, who is described as "A pioneer in the botanical exploration of West Virginia, a discriminative and critical collector, a teacher whose enthusiasm inspired alike his students and associates."

A Bibliography of the Botanical Writings of John L. Sheldon

Plainfield [Conn.] local flora. *Plainfield Journal* 1898.

Asparagus rust in Nebraska. *The Nebraska Farmer* 28:52. 931. 27 D 1900.

Some abnormal flowers. *The American Botanist* 1:5. 66-67. N 1901.

Rooting of Oxalis leaves. *Plant World* 4:11. 201-202. pl. 1. N 1901.

Some plants which live in and upon insects. *Annual Report of the Nebraska State Board of Agriculture.* 1901. 131-141. f. 11.

Notes on the blue-berried huckleberry. *Rhodora* 4:37, 14. Ja 1902.

A carnation disease. *Nebraska Farmer* 33:2. 29 9 Ja 1902.

Botany on the farm. *Agriculture* 1:5. 9-12. Jy 1902.

Preliminary studies on the rusts of the asparagus and the carnation: Parasitism of *Darluca filum. Science* n. s. 16:397. 235-237. 8 Ag 1902.

The "damping-off" disease and its relation to a disease of carnations. *Annual Report of the Nebraska State Horticultural Society.* 1902. 266-269.

Ergot in rye-grass, hay and grain, and its effects on cattle. The Nebraska Farmer 35:8. 202-203. 19 F 1903. *Nebraska Dairyman* 6:10. 2-4. My 1903.

Cultures of *Empusa. Journal of Applied Microscopy and Laboratory Methods* 6:3. 2212-2220. pl. 2. Mr 1903.

Infection and Parasitism of Uredineae. Studies of the Rusts of the Carnations and Asparagus and Parasitism of Darluca Filum. Doctor's Dissertation. Univ. of Nebr. Library. May, 1903.

Twig blight. *West Virginia Farm Review.* 12:2. 41-43. F 1904. 12:8. 232. Ag 1904.

Some introduced weeds of Connecticut. *Rhodora* 6:66. 146. Je 1904.

Diseases of melons and cucumbers during 1903 and 1904. *W. Va. Agr. Exp. Sta. Bull.* 94:121-138. pl. 5. D 1904.

Report on plant diseases of the state. West Virginia. Report of Work of the Experiment Station 1903-1904. 67-93. pl. 6. *W. Va. Agr. Exp. Sta. Bull.* 96:71-99. pl. 6. 30 Je 1905.

A corn mold (*Fusarium moniliforme* n. sp.). *Ann. Rep. Neb. Agr. Exp. Sta.* 17:23-32. illus. 1904.

The ascigerous stage of *Gloeosporium Psidii.* Science n. s. 21:536. 1905.

Nematode galls on clover roots. *West Virginia Farm Review.* 13:2 10 F 1905.

Concerning the identity of the fungi causing an anthracnose of the sweet-pea and the bitter-rot of the apple. *Science* n. s. 22:550. 51-52. 14 Jy 1905.

The effect of different soils on the development of the carnation rust. *Bot. Gaz.* 40:225-229. S 1905.

Report of the Bacteriologist for 1904-5. West Virginia. The Report of the Work of the Experiment Station for the years 1904 and 1905. 26-38.

Clover sickness. *The National Stockman and Farmer* 29:51. 44-45. 29 Mr 1906.

Frog-eye: its cause and effect. *Rep. W. Va. State Board Agr.* for the quarter ending March 31, 1906. 1. 56-62.

The ripe rot or mummy disease of guavas. *W. Va. Agr. Exp. Sta. Bull.* 104:299-315. pl. 4 f. 1. Ap 1906.

Paraphyses in the genus *Glomerella. Science* n. s. 23:596. 851-852. 1 Je 1906.

Tubercles on legumes with and without cultures. *W. Va. Agr. Exp. Sta. Bull.* 105:319-334. 1 Je 1906.

A rare *Uromyces. Torreya* 6:12. 249-250. D 1906.

Report of the Bacteriologist. West Virginia. Report of the Work of the Experiment Station for the years 1905 and 1906. 29-39. pl. 1.

The taxonomy of a leaf-spot fungus of the apple and other fruit trees. *Torreya* 7:7. 142-143. Jy 1907.

A study of the leaf-tip blight of *Draceaena fragrans. Journal of Mycology* 13:138-140. Jy 1907.

Concerning the relationship of *Phyllosticta solitaria* to the fruit blotch of apples. *Science* n. s. 26:658. 183-185. Ag 1907.

Species of Hepaticae known to occur in West Virginia. *Bryologist* 10:80-84. S 1907.

Peach yellows and its control. *Rep. W. Va. State Board Agr.* 22-26. 30 S 1907.

Peach scab. *Rep. W. Va. State Board Agr. for the quarter ending December* 30, 1907. p. 26. Fifteenth Annual meeting of the West Virginia State Horticultural Society, Weston, Dec. 9-10, 1907.

Report on apple diseases. *Same report,* pp. 40-44.

Another leaf-spot fungus of the apple, *Illosporium malifoliorum* sp. nov. *Torreya* 8:6. 139-140. Je 1908.

Notes on Uromyces. *Torreya* 9:54. 1909.

Frog-eye disease of apple leaves. *American Phytopathological Society.* Boston, 1909.

Those Wonderberry Seeds. *Plainfield Journal* Vol. XXIV No. 27, Jan. 27, 1910.

The Andropogon—Viola *Uromyces. Torreya* 10:90. 1910.

Additional localities for Connecticut Hepaticae. *Bryologist* 13:63-64. 1910.

Additional West Virginia Hepaticae. *Bryologist* 13:64-65. 1910.

Menyanthes trifoliata in West Virginia. *Rhodora* 12:11, 12. 1910.

Additions to the recorded mosses of West Virginia. *Bryologist* 15:95-97. 1912.

Some rose anthracnoses. *Phytopathology* 3:70. 1913.

[Contributed to Millspaugh's Flora of West Virginia.] *W. Va. Geological Survey* Vol. V (A). 1913.

[Furnished list of mosses collected in W. Va.] See Nelle Ammons. *Bryologist,* Vol. XXXVII, July-Aug. 1934.

Nematode galls in bryophytes. *Bryologist* Vol. XXXIX, Sept.-Oct. 1936.

[Liverworts collected in W. Va.] See Nelle Ammons. *Bryologist,* Vol. XLI June 1938.

The lichens of West Virginia. *Castanea* 4:75-126. 1939.

It is natural that botanists might wonder why Dr. Sheldon retired at the age of only 54 at perhaps the height of his career. Over a period of years, due to a series of circumstances, Dr. Sheldon had developed a difference of opinion with Dr. James Morton Callahan, Dean of the College of Arts and Sciences, and Dr. Frank Butler Trotter, President of the University. He felt that they did not understand scientific work and expected too much of him. He felt that his work was too heavy. During the war in 1918 he had especially large classes due to the R.O.T.C. training program. In 1919 he was allowed $500 for assistants, but they left to take better positions elsewhere. Qualified people were available but sufficient funds to attract these people were not made available. He also wanted fireproof herbarium cases to replace the wooden ones. Late in September of 1919 he told Dean Callahan to have an assistant for him within a week or

Fig. 7. Fife Cottages, on the campus of West Virginia University, about 1915. The building at the left was for several years occupied by the department of botany, with Dr. Sheldon's office in the front room on the second floor. The back room was the botany laboratory, while bacteriology was taught on the first floor. The building at the right was occupied by the school of medicine, but later was transferred to the botany department. The man standing on the porch is **Martin Loxley Bonar**, professor of pharmacology; the other man is **Robert Clifton Spangler**. The children are **Helen** (who later received a Ph.D. in botany at **Duke University**) and **Max Spangler**, children of **Dr.** and **Mrs. Spangler**.

he would leave. At the end of the week, on October 1, when an assistant had not been employed, he tendered his resignation, packed his personal belongings, including his herbarium specimens and left, never to return to the campus again. He was a serious-minded, conservative, and over-sensitive individual with high ideals, who wanted an up-to-date and efficient department. Dr. Trotter and the Board of Governors apparently felt that they could not meet his demands. It was, of course, very unfortunate for the University to lose the services of a man of the high caliber of Dr. Sheldon.

Throughout the long years of his retirement he never lost his interest in botany. He worked several years, checking about 2000 species of Rev. Gray's collection of lichens of West Virginia, including 118 species new to the State. Former students and associates were always welcomed at his home.

He died on January 15, 1947 at his home in Morgantown. Through the cooperation of his widow, Mrs. Clara Sheldon, his collection of over 5000 specimens was acquired by the University in 1951. In 1952 one of the principal footpaths in the University Arboretum was named the "John Lewis Sheldon Nature Trail" in his honor. (*Arboretum News*, Vol. 2, No. 2, Feb., 1952.)

Dr. Sheldon's wife, Clara Fleming Sheldon, was also a botanist in her own right. She studied under such well-known botanists as Frederic Edward Clements and Charles Edwin Bessey at the University of Nebraska. She did her graduate work for her master's degree under Dr. Sheldon in the newly organized Botany Department of West Virginia University in 1907-08. Although Dr. Sheldon was her teacher he showed no partiality and demanded high standards. She received the first master's degree in botany granted at the University. After the retirement of her husband, Mrs. Sheldon taught in the schools of Monongalia County for twenty-six years, including eighteen years as a biology teacher in Morgantown High School. (See her "Erysiphaceae of West Virginia." *M. S. thesis, W. Va. Univ. Graduate School.* Morgantown, 1908.)

REFERENCES

CORE, EARL L. "The Botanical Exploration of West Virginia," *Proc. W. Va. Acad. Sci.* 10:46-60. 1936.

CORE, EARL L. "John Lewis Sheldon, 1865-1947," *Science* 105:541. 1947.

CORE, EARL L. "Outlines of the Flora of West Virginia." Morgantown: West Virginia University Bookstore, 1954.

CORE, EARL L. "Plant Life of West Virginia." New York: Scholar's Library, 1960.

HUMPHREY, H. B. "Makers of North American Botany." Ronald Press. New York, 1961. (Article on Sheldon).

CHAPTER VII

Perry Daniel Strausbaugh

Perry Daniel Strausbaugh, son of John L. and Fianna (Snavely) Strausbaugh, was born March 21, 1886, on a farm near Republic, Ohio. He received his grade school education in a rural school, District No. 1, Adams Township. During the summer of 1904 he attended North Manchester College for ten weeks, where he received his first preparatory work, including work in botany. He attended Canton College and Bible Institute, Canton, Ohio, during the 1905-06 term, receiving the B. E. (bachelor of English) degree. After continuing his preparatory work at McPherson College during 1906-07 term, he entered Wooster College in 1910, graduating with honors in 1913. He attended the University of Chicago during the summer quarters of 1916 to 1920, and received the degree of doctor of philosophy, cum laude, during the summer quarter of 1920, after attending the two previous years on a research fellowship.

Before entering the teaching profession on a college level, Dr. Strausbaugh had considerable experience in grade school and secondary school teaching. He received a Teachers' Certificate in 1902 and taught in rural schools from 1902 to 1905, and in the grade school at Danville, Ohio, in 1909. He was principal of the Danville-Buckeye City High School during the term of 1909-10, and instructor in the Preparatory School of Wooster College from 1911 to 1913, while he was earning his bachelor's degree. He taught at Wooster College as instructor of biology from 1913 to 1915, as assistant professor of botany from 1915 to 1918 and again during the term of 1920-21, and as professor of botany from 1921 to 1923.

He was married to Mable Mae Ross, of Danville, Ohio, July 21, 1906, to which union was born a son, Warren Laverne on April 21, 1907, and a daughter, Marjorie Glee (now Mrs. Robert J. Heckert) on November 23, 1917. During the early part of his career, before getting established in college work, he had quite a struggle financially. During one period of time he was forced to return home to look after the affairs of his father during his illness and death, and again when his mother-in-law was ill he worked as a day laborer, and cut wood for farmers in the community. At one time or another he sold a very popular combination wire fence tool, Underwood and Underwood Stereoscopes and Stereographs, and wrote life insurance.

In 1923, Dr. Strausbaugh accepted the position as head of the Department of Botany at West Virginia University, and in that year started a career that revolutionized the development of botany in West Virginia. Within a few years time three important developments materialized, the re-establishment of the

Fig. 8. Perry Daniel Strausbaugh

University Herbarium, establishment of the University's "Botanical Expedition," and the founding of Phi Epsilon Phi at the University.

The Herbarium. The West Virginia University Herbarium was originally organized in 1890 by Charles Frederick Millspaugh. When Dr. Millspaugh left the State in 1892, his collection of 1580 numbers remained in the attic of the Experiment Station, and was later moved to Oglebay Hall. No additions were made for many years. Dr. Sheldon, during his tenure at the University, made a large private collection, which was stored in three wooden cases purchased by the Department, but he removed his collection of about 5000 numbers when he retired in 1919.

When Dr. Strausbaugh came to the University in 1923, he found it necessary to make a separate beginning of the University Herbarium, since he felt the herbarium to be an essential feature of every botanical department. Dr. Strausbaugh and Dr. Robert Clifton Spangler, with the assistance of Miss Edith Stevens, began to assemble specimens, storing them in the three large wooden cases, which were at that time completely empty. Dr. Spangler had available several hundred specimens that he had collected in the vicinity of Morgantown from 1912 to 1923. The summer of 1924 was passed in collecting, mounting, and filing these specimens which were to form the nucleus of the present Herbarium.

With the organization of the West Virginia University Botanical Expedition, the Herbarium began to grow rapidly. Hundreds of specimens were added by students working on specific groups or special areas. Many other specimens that had been stored in attics or other out-of-the-way places in the past half-century were salvaged and added to the Herbarium. Remnants of the collections of Dr. Millspaugh and Dr. Sheldon were added, and also a collection of 150 sheets brought together by Dr. L. C. Corbett from New York, West Virginia and South Dakota.

Other important contributions continued to be made to the Herbarium. Mr. L. W. Nuttall, in 1927, donated his valuable collection of about 1000 numbers of vascular plants and about 4000 packets of fungi. Rev. Fred W. Gray, a minister at Marlinton, donated several hundred specimens of lichens, liverworts, and mosses. In 1933 when the departments of botany and zoology were merged with the department of plant pathology to form the new department of biology, the priceless collection of Dr. Millspaugh was added.

In 1939 the cryptogamic collection of the Rev. Mr. Gray, consisting of 20,000 packets of bryophytes and lichens, was acquired by the University. In 1951, Dr. Sheldon's collection of 5000 specimens was also acquired by the University.

Botanical Expedition. In keeping with the general tendency of the time to make larger use of field study and thus give greater emphasis to the observation of plants in their natural setting, the West Virginia University Botanical Expedition was organized by Dr. Strausbaugh in 1926. Thirteen students registered for this first summer field course in botany. With these, Dr. Strausbaugh, Earl L. Core, a graduate assistant, and Ben Harker, a cook, traveled for several weeks over the State in second hand Ford cars, living in tents. This primitive kind of travelling life suggested the name of "gypsy course."

In his journal entry for the first day (June 23) of this pioneer botanical expedition, Mr. Core stated: "Decide to go to Hancock by night for camp. Arrive at Hancock 11 p. m. and are sent to baseball diamond, where we set up cots for women and take to the ground ourselves. Slept badly my first night under the open stars. Our party: P. D. Strausbaugh, Ben Harker, Daisy Chapman, Genevieve Clulo, Lutrell Maclin, Fred Bosely, Ed Gould, L. O. Haynes, Mrs. L. O. Haynes, Kitty Speicher, Jennie Harshbarger, Howard Perine, Nelle Taylor, Winifred Cox, Earl L. Core." On June 24 he further stated: "Breakfasted in Hancock, Md. Crossed Potomac into Morgan Co. Stopped at sandstone quarry. Berkeley Springs, old George Washington property. Washington elm said to have been planted by G. Washington. Saw the springs and baths, old castle built 40 years ago, etc., George Washington property. Drove then over to the Shenandoah over a fine highway most of the way, tar-bound macadam, a link or two under construction but no detours, will be entirely completed between Berkeley Springs and Martinsburg this summer. At Martinsburg for lunch, rain. Drove on out the pike by mistake, back, found Ben, camped at Schadd's Park."

The "Biological Expedition" was described by a member of the 1928 party as follows:[1] "Should you by chance have visited the rear of Science Hall on the first day of summer school, you would have been very anxious to know just what the assemblage of Ford cars, loaded with camping outfits, cooking uten-

[1]Russell G. Sheppard, "See West Virginia Gypsy Fashion." *The W. Va. Agriculturist* (November, 1928), 6-7, 24.

sils, and khaki-dressed students and professor was all about. Upon inquiry you would have been informed that the West Virginia University botanical expedition was soon to launch out upon its third annual tour for the purpose of studying the vegetation of the state in its natural habitat, for collecting new and rare specimens of plants for the University herbarium, and for becoming better acquainted with the state and its people . . . A more enjoyable or beneficial summer cannot be spent by a University student than by going on this expedition . . . 'The Fords' solved the problem of transportation, for they didn't mind being overloaded, and would go between any hills of West Virginia. The cooking was done over an open fire, and the provisions were purchased from, or donated by, the people residing in the locality in which we were camping. Cots were provided inside the tents for those who did not want snakes in their beds, but the majority of the campers preferred the true Indian fashion of rolling up in blankets beneath the stars, as long as they weren't on rocks, or didn't have to pick up their beds and hurry to shelter . . . Everyone enjoyed the camp-fires and numerous ghost stories and many interesting experiences were related around the glowing circle at night by Prof. P. D. Strausbaugh and other members of the 'gang.' . . . The trip was not a sight-seeing one; neither was it a mere vacation, for the value of the information and experience acquired was simply incalculable. As a course in botany or zoology, the trip could hardly be improved upon. To live with plants or animal life for 12 weeks, study them all day and write notes in the evening, it is impossible not to become acquainted with them. As for general information about the state and its people, that could not help coming in incidentally . . . During the three summers the expedition has touched nearly every section of interest in the state, and the most interesting places have been visited each year."

As far as the writer is able to determine, this was the first field course of this character, or at least West Virginia may lay claim to the distinction of having been an early pioneer in the development of this important type of biological work. In 1928, when a class in zoology was added, the name was changed to the West Virginia University Biological Expedition. Both the original Botanical Expedition and later the Biological Expedition received enthusiastic endorsement from some of the leading biologists of the country. Dr. James G. Needham of Cornell University, after having served as professor of zoology with the Expedition for eleven weeks, in speaking of the course, com-

Fig. 9. P. D. Strausbaugh (second from left) and students in Cranberry Glades.

mented: "If there is a better way to study biology, I have not found it." In an article called "Exploring the Streams of West Virginia," in the August, 1931, number of *American Forests,* he states: "We gathered thousands of specimens, accounts of which will appear in scientific papers for decades to come—specimens of plants ranging from oaks to algae; specimens of animals ranging from snakes to sponges—and we saw life in action every day. It is more interesting than life in the laboratory, more informing as to roles and as to functions in natural society. In outdoors nothing lives unto itself alone. The life of the streams is determined by the conditions of the hills that shut them in and feed them. In an unspoiled natural environment two things go together, clean waters and green woods."

Fred E. Brooks, the distinguished French Creek naturalist, stated:[2] "One cannot but be impressed with the fine opportunities which these field trips offer to students who are interested in observing wild plant and animal life just as it carries on in nature. Dried or pickled specimens in a laboratory are necessary for students, but only by seeing a thing where it grows does one become really acquainted with its environment, its associations, its habits and appearance as a living, growing organism."

The influence of the Botanical Expedition has been very great, not only in the training of students in field work, but also in the making of important additions to the knowledge of West Virginia flora.

Phi Epsilon Phi, a national honorary botanical fraternity, was founded at West Virginia University in 1929 by Earl E. Berkley and a small group of botany students, under the direction of Dr. Strausbaugh. Article I, Section 2 of the Constitution states the purpose of the organization as follows: "The purpose of Phi Epsilon Phi shall be to encourage in its members professional spirit by (1) fostering high scholastic attainments during the period of preparation for their profession, and (2) by inciting interest in botanical research.

"To this end, it shall maintain the highest professional ideals, and shall foster fellowship, scholarship, and activity in botanical research."[3]

Membership in the organization is extended to both graduate and undergraduate students in botanical sciences who have met

[2]Fred E. Brooks, "Along our Highways." *West Virginia Review* 8:394. 1931.

[3]The Phi Epsilon Phi National Honorary Botanical Society Bulletin of Information, 1931.

the high scholastic standards required, and to persons on the staff of the institution and other eligible persons through associate and honorary membership classifications.

The spirit and enthusiasm of the charter group spread to other institutions. In 1933 a chapter was installed at Ohio State University. Another, the Gamma Rafinesque, was installed at the University of Kentucky in 1934. In 1950, the Delta Chapter was installed at George Washington University. Chapters have also been installed at other institutions, including DePauw University and Pennsylvania State University.

It is the aim of all chapters to further the education in botany by activities outside of regular course work and to facilitate the exchange of ideas and information and aid in establishing a varied program.

One major activity of Phi Epsilon Phi at the University is the sponsoring of the annual Wild Flower Day for high school students throughout the state. The 24th Annual Wild Flower Day was held May 4, 1963.

GRADUATE STUDENTS. Many students of Dr. Strausbaugh, especially those who had accompanied him on the "Botanical Expedition," filled with an enthusiasm for botanical exploration, have conducted county surveys and studies of specific groups of plants, resulting in significant contributions. It is to this group of individuals that Dr. Strausbaugh gives much credit for the rapid development of a workable Herbarium at the University, and furnishing data for publishing the illustrated *Flora of West Virginia*. The following includes a short biography of a few of his students who have become professional or amateur botanists. Other students are treated elsewhere in this work.

Elizabeth Ann Bartholomew, daughter of Henry E. and Minnie Dell (Brand) Bartholomew, was born June 14, 1912, in Wheeling, West Virginia. She received her elementary education at the Washington Grade School of Wheeling, and her secondary education at Wheeling High School in the commercial curriculum, graduating in 1930. She attended West Virginia University, receiving the bachelor of arts degree in botany in 1934, and the master of arts degree in botany in 1948.

She taught nature study courses at the Wheeling Girl Scout Camp from 1926 to 1938, and was a substitute teacher in the Ohio County Schools from 1935 to 1938. Since 1938 she has been a member of the staff of the Biology Department of West Virginia University, first as herbarium clerk, later as herbarium assistant. In 1963 she was appointed instructor in biology and curator of the Herbarium.

In connection with her work at the Herbarium, "Betty," as she is affectionately called by her many friends, may be thought of as the unofficial ambassador of good-will of the Biology Department. She receives visitors by the hundreds. Some are former students who drop by for a visit, some are students seeking

Fig. 10. P. D. Strausbaugh (left) and Earl L. Core working in the West Virginia University Herbarium on the "Flora of West Virginia". (From West Virginia University Alumni Magazine, Summer, 1947.)

help with some project, and many are University staff members or people from out of town seeking information concerning plant identification.

She is a member of the West Virginia Academy of Science, Southern Appalachian Botanical Club (Secretary since 1936), American Nut Growers Association, Phi Epsilon Phi (Faculty Advisor at present), and Phi Mu. She is also a member of the Wesley Methodist Church of Morgantown, has served as a Girl Scout leader for 21 years, and has assisted in 4-H by teaching nature study classes and writing projects for the State organization. She has served as the Editor of the *Biology Newsletter* at the University for a number of years, and was editor of the West Virginia Academy of Science *Newsletter* in 1960-62.

Betty has collected extensively throughout the state, particularly since 1931 in the Ohio Valley counties, and has contributed notably to the University Herbarium by adding thousands of specimens, including several new records for the state and many new county records. In order to meet the demands of the Conservation Commission and others for help in seed identification, she has started a seed herbarium at the University. At present she has about 350 species.

The principal publications of Miss Bartholomew follow:

Spring foray in the Alleghanies of West Virginia. *Castanea* 4:131-132. 1939.

Three spermatophytes new to West Virginia. *Castanea* 5:111. 1940.

Galium pedemontanum in North America. *Castanea* 6:141-142. 1941.

A. B. Brooks. *Castanea* 9:117-118. 1944.

The flora of Wirt County. *Castanea* 13:145-167. 1948.

The family Hypericaceae in West Virginia. *Castanea* 15:102-110. 1950.

The genus *Botrychium* in West Virginia. *Castanea* 16:135-137. 1951.

Euonymus alatus established in West Virginia. *Castanea* 22:139. 1957.

Papaw in West Virginia. *The Nutshell,* bulletin of the Northern Nutgrowers Association (March, 1953).

Papaw in West Virginia. *Arboretum News* (October, 1953).

Conservation 4-H Project—Spring Wild Flowers. Published by W. Va. State 4-H Office. Morgantown, W. Va. 1957.

Conservation 4-H Project—Summer and Fall Flowers. Published by W. Va. State 4-H Office. Morgantown, W. Va. 1960. Henry Ney Mertz. *Castanea* 28:103-107. 1963.

William Basil Fox was born at Talcott, West Virginia, July 20, 1915. He received his grade school and high school education at Greenbrier Springs and Talcott High School, respectively. He graduated from Talcott High School in 1932, attended Concord College in 1933-1935, and taught in one room grade schools in Summers County in 1935-37. He received the bachelor of science degree at West Virginia University in 1939 and the master of science degree from the same institution in 1940. He received the doctor of philosophy degree from Iowa State University in 1942. During the war, from 1942-1945, he was an instructor in radar in the United States Air Force. After the war he served as assistant agronomist at the Agricultural Experiment Station of Washington, at Pullman (1945-46). In 1946 he joined the staff of North Carolina State College, where he was serving as assistant professor of botany at the time of his death on November 13, 1952, through the accidental discharge of a .22 rifle. At the time of his death he was president of the Southern Appalachian Botanical Club, and at 37 years of age was among the most promising young botanists of the East. He was also a member of the Botanical Society of America, the American Society of Plant Taxonomists, the Association of Southeastern Biologists, and the North Carolina Academy of Sciences. He had published numerous articles on the flora of North Carolina and had studied the *Leguminosae* of Iowa, West Virginia, and North Carolina. He had just returned from a botanical expedition to Baja California.

In 1944 he was married to Helen Lee Hensleigh, who survives him. They had one child, Stephen.

Dr. B. W. Wells, of the botany department of North Carolina State College, said "It has been a terrible blow to all of us here, for Bill was universally held in the highest regard. His course in dendrology was second to none, and as curator of the Herbarium he had enlarged it and increased its efficiency far more than any other contributor had done. Bill will be almost irreplaceable."

Dr. P. D. Strausbaugh commented: "In all of his work he was enthusiastic, persistent, patient, and thorough. Back of his quiet, self-effacing manner there was a strength of character and forcefulness of industry that became so clearly apparent in his altruistic outlook and rich achievement."

Russell Guy Brown was born in Morgantown, West Virginia, January 10, 1905. He attended West Virginia University, majoring in botany and serving as a student assistant in the Botany Department. He received the bachelor of science degree in 1929 and the master of science degree in 1930. He received the doctor of philosophy degree from the University of Maryland in 1934, specializing in plant physiology.

Dr. Brown served as professor of biology and head of the Biology Department at New River State College (now West Virginia Institute of Technology) from 1934 to 1936, and since that time has been a member of the botany staff at the University of Maryland.

He is a member of the Botanical Society of America, Ecological Society of America, and the Southern Appalachian Botanical Club.

Although his major contributions to botany have been in Maryland, while at Montgomery he made careful studies of the flora of Fayette and Kanawha Counties.

Earl Esco Berkley was born at Clayton, West Virginia, July 9, 1902. He attended school at Alderson Junior College and at West Virginia University, where he received his bachelor's degree in 1929. While at the University he assisted Dr. Strausbaugh in the founding of Phi Epsilon Phi, honorary botanical fraternity of the University. He then attended Washington University in St. Louis, receiving the master of science degree in plant physiology in 1930 and the doctor of philosophy degree in plant physiology in 1933. He has since been employed as follows: research chemist of the Cellulose Research Corporation, a subsidiary of the Western Cartridge Company from 1933-1936; a cotton technologist for the U. S. Dept. Agr., 1936-47; fiber technologist, 1947-48; National Cotton Council of America in 1948; and he was then employed by Anderson Clayton Company of Houston, where he was director of their fiber testing and research laboratory until his recent appointment to the Deering Miliken Service Corporation Cotton Department, of Spartanburg, South Carolina.

While a student at West Virginia University and afterwards, Mr. Berkley made an intensive study of the grasses of the State from 1928 to 1934, preliminary to the publication of a bulletin on the subject. (See Core, Earl L., Berkley, Earl E., and Davis, H. A. "West Virginia Grasses," *W. Va. Agr. Exp. Sta. Bull.* 313. 96 p. 1944.)

Henry Lee Dean was born at Cumberland, Maryland, March 13, 1907. After receiving the bachelor of arts degree at West

Virginia University in 1929, he attended Iowa State University, receiving the master of science degree in 1931 and the doctor of philosophy degree in 1936. He served as a student assistant in botany at both institutions. He has been a member of the botany staff of Iowa State University since 1936.

Dr. Dean is a member of the Botanical Society of America, International Society of Plant Morphologists (charter member), fellow of the American Association for the Advancement of Science and of the Iowa Academy of Science, Southern Appalachian Botanical Club, National Association of Botany Teachers, Archeological Society of Ohio, Biological Photographic Association, Gamma Alpha, Sigma Xi, and others.

He has published numerous articles in scientific journals dealing with the genus *Cuscuta;* and has also written laboratory manuals, reviews, abstracts, biographies, magazine articles, etc.

While in West Virginia he made discriminating collections of the West Virginia species of dodder. (See his "Host plants of *Cuscuta Gronovii,*" *Rhodora* 36:372-375. 1934; "Host responses to haustorial invasion of *Cuscuta* species," *Science* n.s. 80:588. 1934.)

Wilbert M. Frye, teacher, amateur botanist, and nut grower, was born at Rio, West Virginia, February 18, 1897. He attended West Virginia University, receiving the bachelor of arts degree in 1927 and the master of arts degree in 1928. After teaching in rural schools for twelve years, he became engaged in horticultural work at Hanging Rock and Pleasant Dale, Hampshire County, West Virginia.

He is a member of the Southern Appalachian Botanical Club, West Virginia Academy of Science, National Geographic Society, and other organizations.

He has contributed notably to the development of the West Virginia University Herbarium through gifts of several thousand specimens since 1928, from Hampshire and surrounding counties, as well as from various states from New York to Florida. He discovered a plant new to science, *Rubus Fryei,* (*Castanea* 18:26. 1953) named in his honor by Davis and Davis. (See his, "The flora of Hampshire County, West Virginia." *Proc. W. Va. Acad. Sci.* 8:59-82. 1935, and "Notes on the flora of South Branch Valley" *Castanea* 7:119-122. 1942.)

Oscar L. Haught was born October 25, 1893 in Jollytown, Pennsylvania. He attended West Virginia University, receiving the bachelor of arts degree in February, 1933 and the master of science degree, in June, 1933. Although Mr. Haught has been engaged in geological work by profession, he has made noteworthy contributions to botany in West Virginia, as well as in Peru, Colombia and Ecuador. In 1931 he made an intensive study of the flora of Wetzel County and has contributed about 900 specimens to the West Virginia University Herbarium. His collections of about 6000 numbers, including about 200 types, from South America, are mainly in the United States National Herbarium, and the Chicago Natural History Museum, and in the National Herbarium of Colombia, in Bogotá. He is a member of the American Association for the Advancement of Science, Geological Society of America, West Virginia Academy of Science, and the Southern Appalachian Botanical Club. His writings deal mainly with geology, published in the West Virginia Geological Survey. (See his "Ecological notes on the vegetation of eastern Wetzel County, W. Va." *Proc. W. Va. Acad. Sci.* 6:43-44. 1933.)

Weldon Wesley Boone was born at Ronceverte, West Virginia, April 20, 1906. He received his grade school education in one-room country schools; graduated from Greenbrier (Ronceverte) High School in 1924; and attended West Virginia University, receiving the bachelor of arts degree in 1929 and the master of science degree in 1935. After attending the University of Minnesota, at the Lake Itasca Biological Station during the summer of 1958 as a fellow of the National Science Foundation, he has attended West Virginia University during the summers of 1959 to 1963, inclusive, as a fellow of the National Science Foundation.

After serving as biology teacher and principal in the high schools of Summers County for twenty-eight years, he has served as principal of Hinton High School since 1959.

He was a charter member of the Southern Appalachian Botanical Club and is a member of the National Association of Biology Teachers.

Since attending the West Virginia University Biological Expedition in 1931, he has been intensely interested in plants. He made a survey of the flora of Summers County in 1933, resulting in a collection of nearly 1000 specimens, most of which were the first authenticated specimens for the County, including about two dozen first records for the State. Since 1933 he has collected several hundred specimens from Summers and surrounding counties, Minnesota, various western states, and in New England states. Most of his collections are in the West Virginia University Herbarium. He has written "Trees of Summers County," 29 pp. Hinton. 1934; and "Vascular flora of Summers County, West Virginia." *W. Va. Univ. Graduate School,* Morgantown. 1961.

Caton N. Hill, of Fairmont, made a botanical survey of Marion County in 1934. (See his "A botanical survey of Marion County, West Virginia," *Proc. W. Va. Acad. Sci.* 8:99-110. 1935.)

Harry Cordray (1910-1948), while a student at the University from 1930 to 1935, made plant collections near his home at Core, and in 1935-36, while in the Barberry Eradication Service, made collections in Monroe and Summers Counties.

Isabelle Lycan Bowling made a study of the flora of Wayne County in 1931. Her collection of 200 sheets is in the University Herbarium.

Peter J. Zucchero, while a member of the biology department of the University in 1931 collected 202 numbers of plants near Morgantown, chiefly in the region near Cheat Lake. (See his "A second record for Asarum grandiflorum in West Virginia" *Castanea* 1:7. 1936.)

Ray Eldridge Harris was born on a farm near Sutton, West Virginia, May 2, 1907. He received his grade school and high school education in the public schools of Braxton County. He received the bachelor of science degree in biology at Marshall College, the master of science degree at West Virginia University, and has done work on the doctoral level at West Virginia University, the University of Chicago, and the University of Virginia.

For several years Mr. Harris served as a biology teacher at Calhoun County High School and at Parkersburg High School. Since 1946 he has been a member of the faculty of Shepherd College, and is now chairman of the Division of Science and Mathematics, and professor of biology.

Mr. Harris studied the flora of Calhoun County in 1932-35, reporting his findings in a master's thesis at the University. His collection of more than 1000 numbers is in the University Herbarium. (See his "Physiographic and floristic ecology of the plant life of Calhoun County." *M. S. thesis, W. Va. Univ. Graduate School,* Morgantown, W. Va. 1935.)

Robert Martin made a study of the plants of Harrison County in 1934. His collection of 124 specimens is in the University Herbarium. (See his "The rushes of West Virginia." *Castanea* 4:39-49. 1939.)

Edgar Boyd Simmons, formerly a teacher in the high school at Moorefield and in 1963 a member of the mathematics staff at Concord College, in 1935 and afterwards made studies of the flora of the South Branch Valley. His collections are in the University Herbarium.

Irvan Speicher, while a member of the West Virginia University Biological Expedition in 1931, collected several hundred numbers of plants for the University Herbarium.

Daisy (Chapman) Dorsey, now a biology teacher at Charleston High School, and well known for her "Dorsey Tours," has made interesting collections of plants of the state, especially in Webster, Morgan, Monongalia, Mineral, Mingo, and Kanawha counties.

Cecil Strickland, of Clendenin, made a study of the flora of his vicinity, depositing his specimens in the West Virginia University Herbarium.

* * * *

Dr. Strausbaugh spent the years of 1942 to 1945 as lieutenant colonel in the Armed Forces. He retired in 1948 and moved to Orlando, Florida. As professor emeritus he has spent several summers at the University working on the *Flora of West Virginia*. Since retirement he has traveled extensively, and has contributed numerous specimens to the University Herbarium from Florida and other states.

Dr. Strausbaugh's wife died April 19, 1959. He was married to Mrs. Dora A. Easterly, of Morgantown, West Virginia, April 14, 1960.

He has been a member of the American Association for the Advancement of Science, American Association of University Professors, American Association of Plant Physiologists, Ecological Society of America, Botanical Society of America, West Virginia Academy of Science (president, 1931-1932), West Virginia State Education Association, Sigma Xi, Phi Beta Kappa, Alpha Gamma Rho, Gamma Alpha, Presbyterian Church, and Morgantown Kiwanis Club (president, 1939).

Before and during retirement Dr. Strausbaugh has kept in touch with many of his former students, and has exhibited genuine concern for their welfare and problems. This can be well illustrated by an excerpt from a letter he wrote to one of his former students in 1931, whose wife had just passed away. "I hope you are feeling much better by this time and that you may be able to restore some of the nervous energy sapped from your reserves by your great sorrow. Time is the greatest factor requisite for the healing of our spiritual wounds and I feel sure that your keen sense of values and your unusually fine judgment will in the course of time, help you to regain your normal equilibrium and enable you to go forward rendering your full measure of service to your fellow men."

A Partial List of the Botanical Publications of Perry Daniel Strausbaugh:

Some troublesome weeds found in water supplies (West Virginia). *W. Va. Eng. Exp. Sta. Tech. Bull.* 2:102-108. 1928.

Plant life of West Virginia. *In, W. Va. Encyclopedia.* W. Va. Publ. Co., Charleston, W. Va. pp. 678-689. 1929.

An invading potato sprout. *Plant Physiology* 4:157-158. 1929.

Common seed plants of the Mid-Appalachian region. 507 pp., Morgantown, W. Va. Edwards Brothers, Ann Arbor, Michigan.

(With Earl L. Core) Some additions to the Millspaugh checklist of West Virginia spermatophytes. *Proc. W. Va. Acad. Sci.* 4:38-48 1930.

(With Earl L. Core and Nelle P. Ammons) Common seed plants of the Mid-Appalachian region. 305 pp. Morgantown, W. Va. 1931. 2nd ed. 1955.

(With Earl L. Core) Phymosia remota. *Rhodora* 34:142-146. 1932.

The West Virginia University Biological Expedition. *The School Journal* 60:6-7. December, 1931.

Cranberry Glades. *Am. Forests* 40:362-364, 382-383. 1934.

(With Earl L. Core) Trees and shrubs of West Virginia. Mimeo. 109 pp., Morgantown, W. Va. 1935.

(With Earl L. Core) Additions to the Millspaugh Checklist of West Virginia spermatophytes. *Proc. W. Va. Acad. Sci.* 9:29-31. 1935.

(With B. R. Weimer) Elements of Biology. J. Wiley and Sons, Inc. New York; London, Chapman & Hall. 1944.

(With G. B. Rigg) Some stages in the development of sphagnum bogs in West Virginia. *Castanea* 14:129-148. 1949.

(With Earl L. Core) Some new or otherwise noteworthy plants from West Virginia. *Castanea* 17:165. 1952.

(With B. R. Weimer) General Biology. Wiley and Sons, Inc., New York. 813 pp. 1938, 1947, 1952.

(With Earl L. Core) Flora of West Virginia, Part I, Equisetaceae-Orchidaceae. *W. Va. Univ. Bull.* Ser. 52, 12-2:1-273. 1952.

(With Earl L. Core) Flora of West Virginia, Part II, Sauru1raceae-Leguminosae. *W. Va. Univ. Bull.* Ser. 53, 12-1:275-570. 1953.

(With Earl L. Core) Flora of West Virginia, Part III, Linaceae-Plantaginaceae. *W. Va. Univ. Bull.* Ser. 58, 12-3:571-860. 1958.

(With Earl L. Core and B. R. Weimer) General Biology. 4th ed. New York, London. 555 pp. 1961.

(With J. G. Needham) At the head of the Cacapon. *Sci. Monthly* 33:80-85. 1931.

(Other publications, without specific reference being given, include, "Dormancy in Plum," in *Botanical Gazette*, his doctor's dissertation; another study of "Dormancy" with Dr. M. J. Dorsey, in *Botanical Gazette;* "Ecology of the LaSalle Region," (Illinois) with Dr. G. D. Fuller, in *Proc. Ill. Acad. Sci.*; hundreds of abstracts in Botanical Abstracts and subsequently in Biological Abstracts; and numerous short notes.)

Honoring Dr. Strausbaugh, the Strausbaugh Trail in the University Arboretum was dedicated in 1955.

REFERENCES

BROOKS, FRED E. "Along our Highways," *West Virginia Review* 8:394. 1931.

CORE, EARL L. "Herbarium Organization at West Virginia University," *Proc. W. Va. Acad. Sci.* 5:61-71. 1931.

CORE, EARL L. Outlines of the Flora of West Virginia. Morgantown: West Virginia University Bookstore, 1954.

CORE, EARL L. Plant Life of West Virginia. New York: Scholar's Library, 1960.

CORE, EARL L., W. H. GILLESPIE AND BETTY J. GILLESPIE. Bibliography of West Virginia Plant Life. New York: Scholar's Library, 1962.

NEEDHAM, JAMES G. "Exploring the Streams of West Virginia," *American Forests* 37:468-469, 511. 1931.

SHEPPARD, RUSSELL G. "See West Virginia Gypsy Fashion," *The West Virginia Agriculturist,* (November, 1928), 6-7, 24.

STRAUSBAUGH, P. D. "The West Virginia University Biological Expedition," *W. Va. School Journal,* December, 1931, 6-7.

CHAPTER VIII

Earl Lemley Core

Earl Lemley Core, Chairman of the Department of Biology of West Virginia University, was born at Core, West Virginia, January 20, 1902, the son of Harry Michael and Clara Edna (Lemley) Core. After receiving his grade school and high school education in the public schools of Monongalia County, he taught in rural schools from 1920 to 1923. He attended West Virginia University, receiving the bachelor of arts degree in 1926 and the master of arts degree in 1928. In 1936 he received the doctor of philosophy degree at Columbia University. In 1957 he was awarded the honorary degree of doctor of science by Waynesburg College, Waynesburg, Pennsylvania.

Since 1926 Dr. Core has been a member of the staff of West Virginia University, as instructor in 1928-34, assistant professor in 1934-41, associate professor in 1941-42, professor since 1942, chairman of the Biology Department since 1948, and curator of the Herbarium since 1934. He was a member of the summer staff of Ohio State University in 1939-41 and of Concord College in 1961, and in 1943-45 was with the Bureau of Economic Warfare, as botanist with the Colombian Cinchona Mission, Bogotá, Colombia.

He was married to Miss Freda Bess Garrison, June 8, 1925, and they are the parents of four children, Ruth (Mrs. Harry Miller), Merle, Harry and David.

Dr. Core has held membership in the following societies, clubs, and other organizations: American Association for Advancement of Science (fellow), Association of Plant Taxonomists, Botanical Society of America (chairman, northeastern section, 1950, and of the southeastern section, 1961), West Virginia Academy of Science, Association of Southeastern Biologists, Southern Appalachian Botanical Club (founded club and its journal, *Castanea,* 1936, president, 1950), Torrey Botanical Club, New York Botanical Garden (Collaborator), Phi Beta Kappa, Wild Flower Preservation Society (editor of *Wild Flower* since 1946), Phi Epsilon Phi, Alpha Gamma Rho, Sigma Xi, and Kiwanis. He is a member of the First Christian Church of Morgantown, and served as president of the State

Convention of Christian Churches (Disciples) of West Virginia in 1959. He has served on the Morgantown City Council and was mayor in 1956-57. Other civic activities include service as chairman of the Morgantown Library Commission, during which period a special levy was approved for construction of a public library building.

It is very difficult to discuss the contributions of Dr. Core to the development of botany in West Virginia, since much

Fig. 11. Earl Lemley Core

of his work has been so closely associated with that of Dr. Strausbaugh. Shortly before his retirement in 1948, Dr. Strausbaugh said: "In 1923-24, my first year in Morgantown, Earl L. Core, a freshman in my botany class, attracted my attention, and the acquaintance ripened into a rare friendship that continues until the present hour—one of the finest experiences of my entire life." As a member of the First Botanical Expedition and afterwards he assisted Dr. Strausbaugh, and the two botanists assembled a mass of data that they later began to publish as an extensive illustrated *Flora of West Virginia,* in four parts. Part I was published in 1952, Part II in 1953, Part III in 1957, and Part IV in 1964.

Within a few years after the re-establishment of the University Herbarium, Dr. Core assisted with its development and has been curator since 1934. "Dr. Earl L. Core, present Chairman of the Biology Department of West Virginia University, has done more collecting in the State, by far, than any other individual."[1] His collections of thousands of numbers from various parts of the state since 1926 has played an important part in the rapid growth of the University Herbarium. He also made extensive collections from the islands of Lake Erie in 1939-41 and the Republic of Colombia in 1943-44.

As a member of the party making up the West Virginia University Botanical Expedition in 1927, he discovered a plant that has been called the rarest plant in the world.[2] It was found on the slopes of Peters Mountain about 1½ miles below the village of Narrows in Giles County, Virginia, and is now known as *Iliamna corei* Sherff.[3] Other plants discovered by Dr. Core in North and South America and named for him include *Ottonia corei* Yuncker (Amer. Jour. Bot. 43:166. 1956), *Cavendishia corei* Smith (Amer. Jour. Bot. 40:474. 1953), *Rubus corei* Bailey (Franz Theo. Stone Lab. Contr. 9:70. 1948), *Senecio corei* Cuatrecasas (Fedde, Rep. Spec. Nov. 55:136. 1953), *Oliganthes corei* Cuatrecasas (Brittonia 8:185. 1956), and *Habracanthus corei* Leonard (Contr. U. S. Natl. Herb. 31:468. 1958).

Three of his most significant and far-reaching contributions have had to do with the formation of the Southern Appalachian

[1]Roy B. Clarkson, *The Vascular Flora of the Monongahela National Forest.* Doctoral Diss. Morgantown: West Virginia University Graduate School. 1960, p. 206.

[2]Rutherford B. Platt, *Our Flowering World,* New York, 1947, p. 210.

[3]*Rhodora* 48:96. 1946; *Amer. Jour. Bot.* 36:503. 1949.

Botanical Club, the part he played in the organization of the West Virginia University Arboretum, previously envisioned by Dr. Millspaugh in 1890, and in the establishment of the Terra Alta Biological Station.

Southern Appalachian Botanical Club. The Southern Appalachian Botanical Club was organized in 1936 by Earl L. Core, with the Biology Department of West Virginia University as its headquarters. As editor of the journal of the club, later named *Castanea,* Dr. Core explained the purpose of the Club as follows:[4] "The region of the Southern Appalachian Mountains is a most interesting and varied one from the standpoint of its phytogeography. Dry shale barrens with endemic species; high cold mountain ranges with southerly extensions of Canadian plants or plants peculiar to the southern highlands; miniature reproductions of northern bogs in the form of mountain glades; valleys pointing back among the hills, carrying far inland the Carolinian and coastal plain species—together form a floral complex replete with the most perplexing and yet enticing problems. The investigation of this most interesting region has until recently been carried on in an intermittent fashion by visiting botanists from the larger centers . . .

"A more careful and systematic investigation of the flora of the region by its permanent residents would doubtless reveal numerous additional new species and significant extensions of ranges, while shedding light on the many intricate problems of phytogeography and plant migrations hidden among the tangled ranges of the Southern Appalachians.

"To this purpose the Southern Appalachian Botanical Club is dedicated."

In February, 1937, the Club had 188 members.[5] By 1964 the membership had grown to about 500, located in all states of the southeast, and in many other regions, including foreign countries. About 150 exchanges of *Castanea* with other botanical institutions are maintained, and the periodicals received in exchange are placed in the Herbarium Library, going to the main University Library for binding upon the completion of volumes.

The Arboretum. West Virginia University acquired the 260-acre Krepps-Dille Farm along the Monongahela River

[4]Earl L. Core, "Foreword," *The Journal of the Southern Appalachian Botanical Club.* 1:1-2. 1936.

[5]See list of members. *The Journal of the Southern Appalachian Botanical Club.* 2:19-26. 1937.

about one mile northwest of the main campus, August 4, 1948. The purpose of this acquisition was to provide space for a Second Campus to relieve crowded conditions on the main

Fig. 12. West Virginia University Arboretum, between Monongahela Boulevard and the Monongahela River, Morgantown.

campus. About 100 acres of the most wooded part of this area was set aside for the West Virginia University Arboretum. President Irvin Stewart appointed an administrative committee with Earl L. Core as chairman. Other members of the committee were W. C. Percival, director of the Division of Forestry, R. S. Marsh, head of the Department of Horticulture, J. G. Leach, head of the Department of Plant Pathology, and J. L. Hayman, dean of the College of Pharmacy. A. M. Miller, superintendent of Buildings and Grounds was added to the committee, and upon his death on January 29, 1953, was succeeded by Edwin Orr. On May 8, 1954 the Arboretum was formally opened and dedicated in public ceremonies. Ray O. Duncan, dean of the School of Physical Education and Athletics, was added to the administrative committee in 1958.

The Arboretum was designed not only as a botanical laboratory for educational purposes but also for its aesthetic and cultural opportunities. It serves as a place for study and research and also for rest and relaxation. It is an out-of-doors museum of plant life with several hundred native plants, as well as hundreds that have been introduced.

The usefulness of the Arboretum to the University and the State of West Virginia might include:[6]

"1. Furnishing living specimens of trees and shrubs for student study, including material for anatomical, physiological, cytological, and other similar uses.

"2. Aiding in the introduction of trees, shrubs and plants, and to test the suitability of various species for planting here.

"3. Helping standardize woody plant names for nurserymen and others.

"4. Disseminating knowledge of species and varieties of plants to the general public.

"5. Making certain local areas more attractive through planting, creating special landscape areas both pleasing and attractive to the public and instructive to students of landscape art."

About 3½ miles of nature trails lead through the area, so arranged that the visitor may take a short walk or a long hike without retracing steps. These are arranged so as to provide a variety of natural habitats.

William Morgan Leeson served as the first Arboretum assistant, followed by Forrest Boggs, George Edward Constable, and

[6]Earl L. Core, "Outlines of the Flora of West Virginia." Morgantown: West Virginia University Bookstore, 1954, p. 116.

Roland Lee Guthrie. In 1963 Mr. Guthrie was appointed director of the Arboretum.

An illustrated offset-printed news sheet, West Virginia University *Arboretum News* is published quarterly and mailed free to nature lovers of the state.

Terra Alta Biological Station. Through the efforts of Dr. Core, and Dr. Herald D. Bennett, with the assistance of other members of the staff, the Terra Alta Biological Station was established during the early part of 1962. The property already belonged to West Virginia University, and had previously been used by the College of Engineering as a surveying camp. Since 1952 the University had maintained a Biological Station at Camp Arthur Wood in conjunction with the Forestry Station, as an outgrowth of the old Biological Expeditions. The location at Camp Wood had been under the direction of Leland H. Taylor, zoologist, who had succeeded Dr. Strausbaugh in charge of the Expeditions.

The first session of the new Station was held from July 23 to August 24, 1962, with Dr. Herald D. Bennett, professor of biology at the University, as director. Dr. Bennett gave courses in Plant Communities and Taxonomy of Vascular Plants. Robert L. Birch, instructor in biology at the University, gave courses in field zoology. Courses in special topics or research were also available.

In his announcement of the opening of the new Biological Station, Dr. Core described the plans, location, and educational possibilities of the Station as follows:[7]

> "Transportation facilities providing access to the Station are excellent. While the Station itself is hidden from view in the center of a 60-acre tract of wooded land, the property borders on a paved road and is only one mile from a main state highway, W. Va. Route 7, with through bus service. The main line of the Baltimore and Ohio Railroad passes through the town of Terra Alta and a passenger depot is located only two miles from the Biological Station. Scheduled plane service is available at the Morgantown airport, an hour's drive away, and a small airport for private planes is located at Terra Alta itself.
>
> "Although to a considerable extent the Station's facilities are of a temporary nature, its basic utilities, including water, sanitation, electricity, gas, and telephone service,

[7]*Castanea* 27:58-59. 1962.

Fig. 13. Terra Alta Biological Station

have already been installed and the educational unit is a "going" concern. Faculty and students will be subjected to some inconveniences for a few seasons, but modern laboratories and residences are being planned to replace temporary buildings now available. The location of the Station, only an hour's drive from the main campus of West Virginia University, renders the libraries, medical center, and other services of the University readily accessible.

"Terra Alta Biological Station is virtually ideally located with respect to the diversified plant and animal habitats of the mid-Appalachian region. Its high Allegheny Mountain situation is less than an hour's drive from forests of spruce and northern hardwoods. The western slopes of the Appalachians, with an annual rainfall up to 65 inches, provide ample opportunities to investigate cove hardwoods and other mixed hardwood forest types. The eastern slopes, with annual rainfall as low as 30 inches, support the more sparse oak-pine forests of the Ridge and Valley province. Fascinating shale barrens, with endemic species, are less than 50 miles away. Aquatic life may be studied in Terra Alta Lake, a 5-minute walk from the Station, or in Deep Creek Lake, 20 miles away in Garrett County, Maryland. For stream studies there is Cheat River, 10 miles to the west, or the Potomac River, with numerous large tributaries, only a few miles to the east. Interesting bog communities are in Cranesville Swamp Nature Sanctuary, 8 miles from the Station, where an 'island' of northern life exists as a relict colony in a southern latitude. Spruce Knob (elev. 4,860 ft.), the highest point in West Virginia, is about 75 miles by road south of the Station. Intriguing grassy balds, as yet inexplicable, and desolate heath barrens, on the high Appalachian summits, are accessible by automobile . . .

"Interesting geological outcrops, from Cambrian to Permian, provide habitats for wide diversification of plant and animal life. Limestone, sandstone, and shale formations are abundant, while more unusual quartzite and other formations are available for study. Natural features of biological as well as general interest within relatively short distances from the Station include Blackwater Falls, Canaan Valley, Sinks of Gandy, Blister Swamp, Bald Knob, Roaring Plains, Dolly Sods, Seneca Rocks, Seneca Caverns, the

Smoke Hole, the Trough, Ice Mountain, and Greenland Gap. Elevations that may be reached within a 3-hour drive from the Station range from 240 feet above sea level at Harpers Ferry National Monument to 4,860 feet on the summit of Spruce Knob."

Space will permit mention of only a representative number of Dr. Core's students. Several of these students worked jointly with Dr. Strausbaugh and Dr. Core. Three students, Melvin Leslie Brown, Charles Leslie Bryner, and Nathan William Easterly, received the degree of doctor of philosophy in botany in 1957, the first to be awarded in botany in West Virginia.

Melvin Leslie Brown was born at Emoryville, West Virginia, November 16, 1918. After graduating from Elk Garden High School, he attended Potomac State College, Shepherd College, and received the bachelor of science degree at Fairmont State College in 1944. He attended West Virginia University, receiving the master of science degree in 1948 and the doctor of philosophy degree in 1957.

After teaching four and a half years in Mineral County, West Virginia, he has taught in several high schools in Maryland, and in 1963 was teaching biology in a high school at Frostburg, Maryland. He also taught in the Biology Department of West Virginia University during the summer sessions of 1959 and 1960.

Dr. Brown is a member of Sigma Xi, West Virginia Academy of Science, Phi Epsilon Phi, and the Southern Appalachian Botanical Club.

He has contributed about 1000 numbers of plant specimens, mostly from Mineral County, to the West Virginia University Herbarium. (See his, "A floristic study of Mineral County." *Diss., W. Va. Univ. Graduate School,* Morgantown. 1957.)

Charles Leslie Bryner was born on October 15, 1914, near Dunbar, Pennsylvania. He received his early education in the public schools of Dunbar Township. After receiving his bachelor of science degree from Waynesburg College, he later attended West Virginia University, receiving the master of science degree in 1948 and the doctor of philosophy degree in 1957.

For two years he was a teacher and supervising principal in the Dunbar Borough School District, but resigned at the beginning of World War II to enlist in the United States Navy, where he served four years as a commanding officer. He then accepted a position as instructor at Waynesburg College, and in 1963 was head of the biology department at this institution.

He has done considerable collecting in West Virginia, and a number of his specimens are in the West Virginia University Herbarium.

He has written the following: "Botanical exploration in West Virginia by Edward Strieby Steele." *Proc. W. Va. Acad. Sci.* 27:32-34. 1955 (1956); "Prophet without honor: Life and botanical contributions of Edward Strieby Steele." *Diss., W. Va. Univ. Graduate School*, Morgantown, W. Va. 1957.

Nathan William Easterly was born September 9, 1927 at White Sulphur Springs, West Virginia. He received the bachelor of arts degree at West Virginia University, the master of science degree at the University of Iowa, and the doctor of philosophy degree at West Virginia University in 1957.

Since 1957 Dr. Easterly has been a member of the biology staff at Bowling Green State University, Bowling Green, Ohio.

He is a member of the Botanical Society of America, American Institute of Biological Science, Brooklyn Botanical Garden, and the Southern Appalachian Botanical Club. He is a member of the Kiwanis Club and the Methodist Church.

His doctoral dissertation, "A morphological study of the genus *Ptilimnium*," constitutes an important contribution to botanical knowledge. This was based on research conducted under the direction of H. D. Bennett. Other writings include, "The family Cruciferae in the Great Black Swamp region of Ohio." *Ohio Jour. Sci.* 60(1):55, January, 1960, and "Chromosome numbers of some northwestern Ohio Cruciferae." *Castanea* 28:39-42. 1963. He has contributed specimens to various herbaria, including the West Virginia University Herbarium.

William Morgan Leeson was born on August 31, 1927, at Fairmont, West Virginia, and received his grade school and high school education in that city. After spending one year at West Virginia University in 1944 he entered the United States Navy. After about two years in the Navy, he resumed his college work at Fairmont State College in June, 1947. In September, 1947, he returned to the University, receiving the bachelor of arts degree in 1950 and the master of science degree in botany in 1951. In connection with his master's thesis which dealt with the original vegetation of the new University Arboretum he made a very thorough botanical survey of the area. This thesis gives a detailed description of the Arboretum and a list of all the native plants which he found, including 79 families and 304 species. He served as arboretum assistant from 1952 to 1954.

Robert Marshall Tetrick II (1929-1950), was born June 9, 1929, near Buckhannon, W. Va. He was an honor student at Buckhannon High School and graduated in 1947. He received a scholarship at West Virginia Wesleyan College and attended for one year. He attended West Virginia University for two years, and during the summer of 1950 as a member of the West Virginia University Biological Expedition under the direction of Dr. E. Meade McNeill, while stationed at Camp Summers, near Hinton, drowned on June 23 in Greenbrier River.

He was an ardent student of ferns and fern allies. For his age he was no doubt the outstanding fern student in West Virginia. He was a careful observer and classifier and paid especial attention to the many fern variations. Several of his specimens are in the University Herbarium. (See his, "*Botrychium* range extensions in West Virginia." *Am. Fern Jour.* 38:93. 1948; and "A new form of the brown stem spleenwort." *Am. Fern Jour.* 39:92-93. 1949.)

James C. Myers was born August 30, 1918 in Fairmont, West Virginia. He received the bachelor of arts degree and master of science degree from West Virginia University, and has had course work in botany in the universities of Ohio State, Michigan, and Illinois. He also has the master of science degree in library science from the University of Illinois. He is now engaged in library work at Florida State University, Tallahassee, Florida.

He is a member of Sigma Xi, Southern Appalachian Botanical Club, as well as the Southeastern Library Association, and Florida Library Association. He has made extensive collections of plants from West Virginia, Ohio, Michigan, and French Morocco.

Although Mr. Myers got sidetracked after the war and into another field, he still has a warm feeling for botany and botanists, and is still contributing to the West Virginia University Herbarium. (See his, "The Polygonaceae of West Virginia." *Castanea* 6:37-52. 1941; "A new variety of *Polygonum pensylvanicum* L." *Castanea* 7:74-75. 1942, and "The genus *Hieracium* in West Virginia." *Castanea* 15:92-101. 1950.)

George E. Constable was born at Fairmont, West Virginia, April 29, 1919. He received his elementary education at the Thomas C. Miller Grade and Junior High School of Fairmont, and his secondary education at Fairmont West High School. He received the bachelor of science degree from Fairmont State

College, and the master of science degree from West Virginia University.

He served as Arboretum assistant from 1955 to 1959. He was professor of biology at Frostburg State Teachers College in 1959-1960, and in 1963 was teaching in Florida.

He is a member of Phi Epsilon Phi, West Virginia Academy of Science, Southern Appalachian Botanical Club, and numerous community organizations.

His collections of hundreds of specimens from Taylor, Marion, Harrison, and Greenbrier counties are in the University Herbarium.

He has written as follows: "The flora of Taylor County, West Virginia." *M. S. thesis, W. Va. Univ. Graduate School,* Morgantown, W. Va. 1959; "The Tygart Valley Falls, West Virginia." *Castanea* 25:101-103. 1960; "Dr. Millspaugh's Trillium." *Wild Flower* 37:31-33. 1961.

He has contributed numerous articles to the *Arboretum Newsletter* and is author of "Trail Guide to the West Virginia Arboretum" (1958), and "Trail Guide to the Brooks Memorial Arboretum, Watoga State Park" (1957).

Arthur Wayne Vincent was born at Colfax, West Virginia, February 16, 1925. He attended Fairmont State College, receiving the bachelor of science degree in 1948 and the bachelor of arts degree in 1949. He received the master of science degree at West Virginia University in 1958.

After teaching in high school for nine years, he became associated with Henry Holt and Company as a textbook salesman.

In connection with his graduate work at the University, he made a thorough study of the mint family in West Virginia. (See his master's thesis, "Labiatae of West Virginia." *W. Va. Univ. Graduate School,* Morgantown, W. Va. 1957.)

William Alan Lunk was born May 6, 1919 in Johnstown, Pennsylvania. He attended West Virginia University, receiving his bachelor's degree in zoology in 1941 and his master's degree in 1946. He received the doctor of philosophy degree from the University of Michigan in 1955. He was an instructor in biology at West Virginia University in 1946-47, and since 1949 has been connected with the Exhibit Museum of the University of Michigan as associate curator of exhibits. He is a member of the American Ornithologists' Union, Wilson Ornithology Society, Southern Appalachian Botanical Club, American Society of Mammalogists, Sigma Xi, Phi Epsilon Phi, and Society of Vertebrate Paleontology.

Although Dr. Lunk is a zoologist, he has written "Rubiaceae of West Virginia." *Castanea* 12:27-38. 1947. He has made important botanical contributions in the way of scientific illustrations for the work of others as follows: Core, Earl L. 1948. "Spring Wild Flowers,"; Strausbaugh, P. D. and Earl L. Core, "Flora of West Virginia." Part 1 (1952), Part 2 (1953), Part 3 (1958) and Part 4 (1964); Core, Earl L. 1955. "Plant Taxonomy,"; and Gillespie, William H. 1959. "Edible Wild Plants."

Orris D. McCauley was born in Rock Cave, West Virginia, February 9, 1922. He received the bachelor of science degree in forestry at West Virginia University in 1949, and his master of science degree in botany from the same institution in 1950, and had one year of graduate work in botany at Indiana University in 1950 and 1951. He served in the United States Army from 1940 to 1945 and 1951 to 1954. He worked for the West Virginia Conservation Commission during the summers of 1949 and 1950, was graduate assistant in the Biology Department of West Virginia University from 1948 to 1950, science teacher, Plain City High School in Plain City, Ohio, 1954-56, and has been connected with the United States Forest Service, Central States Experiment Station, as resident forester since 1956.

He is a member of the Society of American Foresters, American Marketing Association, Southern Appalachian Botanical Club, Phi Epsilon Phi, and Sigma Xi.

He contributed approximately 600 numbers to the West Virginia University Herbarium in 1949-50. (See his: "The woody plants of Cooper's Rock State Forest." *M. S. thesis, W. Va. Univ. Graduate School,* Morgantown, W. Va. 1950; also published in *Castanea* 16:49-63. 1951.) He also has about ten other publications in the field of Forest Economics.

Percy Lane Lilly was born in Spanishburg, West Virginia, July 14, 1927. He received his bachelor of science degree from Concord College, the master of science degree from West Virginia University, and the doctor of philosophy degree from Pennsylvania State University, and did additional study at Indiana University. He served as instructor of biology at Salem College for two years, teaching assistant at Pennsylvania State University for three years, and as professor of biology at Heidelberg College since 1956.

He is a member of Sigma Xi, Ohio Academy of Science, Botanical Society of America, and Ohio Conference of College Biology Teachers.

He has contributed about 100 specimens to the West Virginia University Herbarium, about 1000 numbers to Heidelberg College and 200 to Pennsylvania State University. (See his "Flora of Mercer County, West Virginia." *M. S. thesis, W. Va. Univ. Graduate School,* Morgantown, W. Va. 1951.)

Roland Lee Guthrie was born at Charleston, West Virginia, April 5, 1928. He attended West Virginia University, receiving the bachelor of science degree in forestry in 1953 and the master of science degree in botany in the same year, submitting as his master's thesis a study of the plants of the Ripley conference center. He became Arboretum assistant in 1959 and director of the Arboretum in 1963. In addition to his duties with the Arboretum, he also assists with dendrology classes. He assisted materially in the acquisition (in 1960) by The Nature Conservancy, Inc., of the Cranesville Swamp Nature Sanctuary, now administered in connection with the University Arboretum (see his "Preservation of Cranesville Swamp" *Proc. W. Va. Acad. Sci.* 34:13-15. 1962), and in the organization (in 1963) of the West Virginia chapter of The Nature Conservancy.

William Harry Gillespie was born January 8, 1931, at Webster Springs, West Virginia. He graduated from Webster Springs High School in 1948. He attended West Virginia University, receiving the bachelor of science degree in forestry in 1952, and the master of science degree in botany in 1954, using as the subject for his thesis, "The poisonous plants of West Virginia."

Mr. Gillespie in 1963 was connected with the plant pest control division of the West Virginia Department of Agriculture, Morgantown, West Virginia. He has pursued his interest in botany and has written as follows:

A compilation of the edible wild plants of West Virginia. Mimeo. Herbarium, W. Va. Univ., Morgantown, W. Va. 70 pp. 1951.

Trichomanes Boschianum in West Virginia. *Amer. Fern Jour.* 45:118-119. 1955.

West Virginia's largest sycamore. *Castanea* 20:72-73. 1955.

The largest sycamore in the United States. *Charleston Gazette Suppl.—"State Magazine,"* May 8, 1955.

Edible wild plants of West Virginia. *W. Va. Garden News,* June issue. pp. 14-15, 30. 1956.

Recent extensive mortality of scarlet oak in West Virginia. *Plant Disease Rept.* 40:1121-1123. 1956.

A compilation of the edible plants of West Virginia. Illus. Scholar's Library, N. Y. 120 pp. 1959.

Observations on scarlet oak mortality in eastern West Virginia. *Phytopathology* 47:13. 1956.

(With I. S. Latimer, Jr.) History and bibliography of West Virginia Paleobotany. *Castanea* 26(4). Contains a complete bibliography to January 1961.)

(With Core, Earl L. and Betty J. Gillespie) Bibliography of West Virginia plant life. Scholar's Library, N. Y. 46 pp. 1962.

A partial list of recent graduate students at West Virginia University and whose master's theses concern botany of the State includes:

Ruth Bush DeMoss, 1950. The influence of botany on West Virginia place names.

Harvey Eugene Wildman, 1950. The pollination of *Asarum canadense.*

Alice L. Fodor, 1951. Flora of Randolph County, West Virginia.

William David Kolb, 1951. Associations under West Virginia forest cover types.

Roy E. Snyder, 1951. Vegetation pattern of a belt transect analysis at Cooper's Rock in northern West Virginia.

William Malcolm Selvey, 1952. The natural history of the Appalachian region as observed by George Washington.

Glenn Orrick Workman, Jr., 1952. Types of vegetation growing on the different strata of rocks in Mineral County, West Virginia.

Forrest J. Boggs, 1953. Flora of Braxton County.

Joseph Theodore Galusky. 1955. Flora of Preston County, West Virginia.

Marian Robison Clark, 1956. The medicinal plants of West Virginia.

Joseph Francis Glencoe, Jr., 1961. *Spiraea virginiana* Britton; a rare southern Appalachian endemic.

John Bonar, 1963. Flora of Brooke and Hancock Counties.

* * * *

Unquestionably, Dr. Core has written more botanical books and articles, dealing chiefly with the Appalachian region, than any other West Virginian. His bibliography follows:

Ecological Studies on Spruce Mountain. *Proc. W. Va. Acad. Sci.* 2:36-39. 1928.

The Plant Ecology of a Type Area in northern West Virginia. *Proc. W. Va. Acad. Sci.* 2:40-43. 1928.

Plant Ecology of Spruce Mountain, West Virginia. *Ecology* 10:1-13. 1929.

(With P. D. Strausbaugh) Some additions to the Millspaugh check-list of West Virginia Spermatophytes. *Proc. W. Va. Acad. Sci.* 4:38-48. 1930.

Herbarium Organization at West Virginia University. *Proc. W. Va. Acad. Sci.* 5:61-71. 1931.

(With P. D. Strausbaugh and Nelle Ammons) Common Seed Plants of the Mid-Appalachian Region. xxiv + 305 p. Morgantown. 1931. 2nd ed. 1955.

Some Aspects of the Phytogeography of West Virginia. *Torreya* 32:65-71. 1932.

(With P. D. Strausbaugh) *Phymosia remota. Rhodora* 34:142-146. 1932.

Studies in the genus Scleria. *Brittonia* 1:239-243. 1934.

The Blister Pine in West Virginia. *Torreya* 34:92, 93. 1934.

(With P. D. Strausbaugh) West Virginia Trees and Shrubs. Mimeographed. 109 p. Morgantown. 1935.

Contributions of Charles Frederick Millspaugh to the Botany of West Virginia. *Proc. W. Va. Acad. Sci.* 8:82-93. 1935.

A Syllabus of the Spermatophyta. Mimeographed. 146 p. Morgantown. 1935. 2nd ed. 1948.

The American Species of Scleria. *Brittonia* 2:1-105. 1936.

(With P. D. Strausbaugh) Additions to the Millspaugh Check-list of West Virginia Spermatophytes. *Proc. W. Va. Acad. Sci.* 9:29-31. 1936.

The Type Localities of some Plants first described from West Virginia. *Torreya* 36:7-13. 1936.

The genus Carex in West Virginia. *Proc. W. Va. Acad. Sci.* 11:29-43. 1937.

Spring Foray to Blackwater Falls and Spruce Knob, West Virginia. *Castanea* 2:87, 88. 1937.

Joint Trip with the Southern Appalachian Botanical Club in southern New Jersey. *Torreya* 37:130-132. 1937.

Joint Foray at Lancaster, Pennsylvania, June 15-19. *Castanea* 3:79-81. 1938.

Plant Migrations and Vegetational History of the Southern Appalachian Region. *Lilloa* 3:5-29. 1938.

John Kunkel Small. *Castanea* 3:27, 28. 1938.

Raymond H. Torrey. *Castanea* 4:6, 7. 1939.

Review of *Climatic Variations. Castanea* 4:9. 1939.

Gum Springs Bog. *Castanea* 4:7, 8. 1939.

A Taxonomic Revision of the genus Siphonychia. *Jour. Elisha Mitchell Sci. Soc.* 55:339-345. 1939.

The Flora of Roaring Plains, West Virginia. *Proc. W. Va. Acad. Sci.* 12:33-35. 1939.

Plant Names (book review). *Castanea* 5:13, 14. 1940.

(With H. A. Davis) Spermatophytes new to West Virginia. *Castanea* 5:20-23. 1940.

Notes on the mid-Appalachian Species of Paronychia. *Va. Jour. Sci.* 1:110-116. 1940.

A Catalog of the Vascular Plants of West Virginia. *Castanea* 5:29-68. 1940.

The Shale Barren Flora of West Virginia. *Proc. W. Va. Acad. Sci.* 14:27-36. 1940.

Travels of Asa Gray in western Virginia, 1843. *Rhodora* 42:344-351. 1940.

Our Native Shrubs. *Extension Landscape Newsletter* (Morgantown) Jan. 1941.

A new Species of Paronychia from Mexico. *Madroño* 6:21, 22. 1941.

Butomus umbellatus in America. *Ohio Jour. Sci.* 41:79-85. 1941.

Notes on some West Virginia Plants. *Castanea* 6:86-88. 1941.

The North American Species of Paronychia. *Amer. Midl. Nat.* 26:369-397. 1941.

(With H. A. Davis) Additions to the Catalogue of the Vascular Plants of West Virginia, I. *Proc. W. Va. Acad. Sci.* 15:73-76. 1941.

Another Clute Book on Common Names. (book review). *Castanea* 7:75, 76. 1942.

(With H. A. Davis) Additions to the Catalogue of the Vascular Plants of West Virginia, II. *Proc. W. Va. Acad. Sci.* 16:35-40. 1942.

The genus Scleria in extra-tropical South America. *Lilloa* 8:535-544. 1942.

Book Review: Textbook of Botany by E. N. Transeau, H. C. Sampson and L. H. Tiffany. *Jour. Amer. Soc. Agron.* 34:203. 1942.

Botanizing in the Higher Alleghenies. *Scientific Monthly* 57:119-125. 1943.

Plants we eat and wear (book review). *Castanea* 8:79. 1943.

(With Bernal R. Weimer) A new manual for the Biology Laboratory. New York. 216 p. 1944. 2nd ed. 1952.

(With Earl E. Berkley and H. A. Davis) West Virginia Grasses. *W. Va. Agr. Exper. Sta. Bull.* 313:1-96. 1944.

(With H. A. Davis) Additions to the Catalogue of the Vascular Plants of West Virginia, III. *Proc. W. Va. Acad. Sci.* 17:27-30. 1945.

Two new species of Scleria from the upper Amazon Valley. *Jour. Wash. Acad. Sci.* 35:322. 1945.

Book Review: The Southern Appalachians. *Castanea* 10:31, 32. 1945.

(With Nelle Ammons) The Hollies of West Virginia. *Castanea* 10:57-60. 1945.

(With Nelle Ammons) The Dogwoods of West Virginia. *Castanea* 10:88-91. 1945.

(With Nelle Ammons) Huckleberries, Blueberries and Cranberries of West Virginia. *Castanea* 10:103-109. 1945.

Ramps. *Castanea* 10:110-112. 1945.

On the Need for Revision of the International Code of Botanical Nomenclature. *Castanea* 10:116-119. 1945.

The Southern Appalachian Botanical Club: Past and Future. *Castanea* 10:119, 120. 1945.

(With Nelle Ammons) Woody Plants of West Virginia in Winter Condition. Lithoprinted. 124 p. 269 figs. Ann Arbor. 1946.

The Gardens of Colombia. *W. Va. Garden Club News* 10:10-12. 1945; 10:14, 15. 1946.

Wild Flowers of the Appalachian Shale Barrens. *Wild Flower* 22:13-18. 1946.

The genus Scleria in Cuba. *Mem. Soc. Cubana Hist. Nat. Felipe poey* 18:43-56. 1946.

Scleria (in *Flora de Cuba,* pp. 230-235.) 1946.

(With H. A. Davis) Additions to the Catalogue of the Vascular Plants of West Virginia, IV. *Proc. W. Va. Acad. Sci.* 18:26-29. 1947.

John Lewis Sheldon. 1865-1947. *Science* 105:541. 1947.

The Flora of the Erie Islands. *Franz Theo. Stone Lab. Contr.* No. 9 viii + 107 p. 1948.

Spring Wild Flowers. iv + 100 p. W. Va. Conserv. Comm. 1948. 2nd ed. 1958.

The genus Scleria in Colombia. *Caldasia* 5:17-32. 1948.

(With H. A. Davis) Additions to the Catalogue of the Vascular Plants of West Virginia, V. *Proc. W. Va. Acad. Sci.* 19:23-26. 1949.

(With H. A. Davis) Additions to the Catalogue of the Vascular Plants of West Virginia, VI. *Proc. W. Va. Acad. Sci.* 20:39-45. 1949.

(With H. A. Davis) Additions to the Catalogue of the Vascular Plants of West Virginia, VII. *Proc. W. Va. Acad. Sci.* 21:52-56. 1949.

Man's First Gardens. *Garden Gleanings.* 3:No. 8; No. 9:2, 3, 8, 9. 1949.

American Wild Flowers (Book Review) *Castanea* 14:149-150. 1949.

Notes on the Plant Geography of West Virginia. *Castanea* 15:61-79. 1950.

A New Textbook in Botany. (Book Review) *Castanea* 15:138, 139. 1950.

It was worth waiting for! (Review of Gray's Manual of Botany, 8th Edition) *Castanea* 15:139-141. 1950.

A Checklist of the Vascular Plants of West Virginia. Mimeographed iii + 69 + 2. Morgantown. 1950.

(With H. A. Davis) Additions to the Catalogue of the Vascular Plants of West Virginia, VIII. *Proc. W. Va. Acad. Sci.* 22:54, 55. 1951.

Botanizing in the Northern Andes. *Wild Flower* 27:6-20. 4 pl. 1951.

The New Arboretum. *West Virginia University Alumni Magazine* 16:4, 21, 22. 1951.

Scleria tepuiensis Core sp. nov. (in Steyermark, Contributions to the Flora of Venezuela) *Fieldiana* 28:52. 1951.

Joseph E. Harned. *Castanea* 16:78, 79. 1951.

The Revised Grass Manual (Book Review). *Castanea* 16:82, 83. 1951.

Danske Dandridge. *Castanea* 16:138-142. 1951.

Botanizing on Panther Knob, West Virginia. *Wild Flower* 28:35-38. 6 pl. 1952.

The Ranges of some plants of the Appalachian shale barrens. *Castanea* 17:105-116. 1952.

Lawrence William Nuttall. *Castanea* 17:157-164. 1952.

(With P. D. Strausbaugh) Some new or otherwise noteworthy plants from West Virginia. *Castanea* 17:165. 1952.

(With P. D. Strausbaugh) Flora of West Virginia, Part 1. *W. Va. Univ. Bull.* 273 p. 1952.

The Southern Appalachian Botanical Club in 1953. I. History of the Club and its journal, Castanea. *Asa Gray Bulletin, n.s.* 2:199: 1953.

Pendleton County, West Virginia. *Tribio* 2:3, 4. 1953.

(With H. A. Davis) New plant records for West Virginia. *Castanea* 18:31. 1953.

The new Britton & Brown (Book Review) *Castanea* 18:34, 35. 1953.

(With P. D. Strausbaugh) Flora of West Virginia, Part 2. *W. Va. Univ. Bull.* pp. 275-570. 1953.

The genus Scleria in Brazil. *Rodriguesia* XV (27):137-162. 1952.

Wild Flowers of Western Pennsylvania and the Upper Ohio Basin (book review). *Bull. Torr. Bot. Club* 81: 471, 472. 1954.

Woody plants of the southwestern deserts (book review) *Castanea* 19:107, 108. 1954.

The ecology of Lake Erie (book review) *Castanea* 19:128. 1954.

An unusual regional book on ferns (book review) *Castanea* 20:74, 75. 1955.

A new edition of an old text (book review) *Castanea* 20:75, 76. 1955.

Vascular Plants of Illinois (book review) *Castanea* 20:128, 129. 1955.

A new edition of Schuyler Mathews' American Wild Flowers (book review) *Castanea* 20:129-131. 1955.

Cranberry Glades Natural Area. *Wild Flower* 31:65-81. 1955.

Outlines of the Flora of West Virginia. Mimeographed. 149 p. Morgantown, W. Va. 1954.

Plant Taxonomy. 459 pp. Prentice-Hall, Inc. Englewood Cliffs, N. J. 1955.

Scutellaria ovata in West Virginia. *Castanea* 22(4):139, 140. 1957.

The Garden of Chaparral (book review) *Castanea* 23:113, 114. 1958.

Flora of Manitoba (book review) *Castanea* 23:116, 117. 1958.

Spring Flora of North-Central Texas (book review) *Castanea* 23:117, 118. 1958.

(With P. D. Strausbaugh) Flora of West Virginia. Part 3. *W. Va. Univ. Bull.*, pp. 571-860. 1958.

(With Nelle Ammons) Woody Plants in Winter. 218 p. Pittsburgh. 1958.

Fundamentals of Plant Physiology (book review). *Castanea* 24:134. 1959.

(et al) Biological Investigations of Cheat Lake. 39 p. Morgantown. 1959.

Articles on Arbutus, Bloodroot, Calendula, Boehmeria, Cinquefoil, Duckweed, Fireweed, Indian Paintbrush, Lungwort, Meadow Beauty, Milkweed, Oregon Grape, Ranunculus, Smartweed, Solomon's Seal, Spurge Family, and Toadflax, in *World Book Encyclopedia.* 1960.

Wild Flowers of Texas (book review) *Castanea* 25:67. 1960.

Plant Life of West Virginia. 224 p. Scholar's Library. New York, N. Y. 1960.

Articles on Arboretum, Botanical Gardens, Herbarium, Plant Keys, Plant Names, Plant Taxonomic Literature, in *McGraw-Hill Encyclopedia of Science and Technology*. 1960.

The Biology of Sherlock Holmes (book review) *Castanea* 25:88. 1960.

Taxonomy of the Flowering Plants (book review) *Castanea* 25:88. 1960.

Drawings of British Plants (book review) *Castanea* 25:107. 1960.

(With John H. Rietz and William H. Gillespie) The Poisonous Plants of West Virginia. 91 p. Illus. *W. Va. Dept. Agri.* [1961].

Drawings of British Plants (book review) *Castanea* 26:106. 1961.

Articles on Herbarium, Rhamnales in *Reinhold Encyclopedia of the Biological Sciences*. 1961.

(With P. D. Strausbaugh and B. R. Weimer) General Biology. 4th edition. New York, London. 555 p. 1961.

(With B. R. Weimer and R. B. Clarkson) A new Manual for the Biology Laboratory. 3d edition. 263 p. New York, London. 1961.

The varieties of *Rudbeckia hirta*. *Castanea* 27:61-62. 1962.

Terra Alta Biological Station. *Castanea* 27:57-59. 1962.

(With Gillespie, William H. and Betty J. Gillespie) Bibliography of West Virginia plant life. New York. Scholar's Library. 1962.

REFERENCES

CLARKSON, ROY B. "The Vascular Flora of the Monongahela National Forest." Diss. Morgantown: West Virginia University Graduate School, 1960.

CORE, EARL L. "Herbarium Organization at West Virginia University," *Proc. W. Va. Acad. Sci.* 5:61-71. 1931.

CORE, EARL L. "Foreword," *Jour. S. Appal. Bot. Club* 1:1-2. 1936.

CORE, EARL L. "Outlines of the Flora of West Virginia." Morgantown: West Virginia University Bookstore, 1954.

CORE, EARL L. "Plant Life of West Virginia." New York: Scholar's Library, 1960.

CORE, EARL L. "Terra Alta Biological Station," *Castanea* 27:58-59. 1962.

CORE, EARL L., WILLIAM H. GILLESPIE AND BETTY J. GILLESPIE. "Bibliography of West Virginia Plant Life." New York: Scholar's Library, 1962.

SHERFF, EDWARD EARL. "Notes on Certain Plants in the Gray's Manual Range." *Rhodora* 48:96. 1946.

STRAUSBAUGH, P. D. AND EARL L. CORE. *"Phymosia remota,"* *Rhodora* 34:142-146. 1932.

CHAPTER IX

The Brooks Family

Unquestionably the best known and most distinguished family of naturalists in West Virginia has been the Brooks Family, of French Creek. Their trips into the virgin forests of the Appalachian Mountains yielded much valuable information and they were frequently accompanied by naturalists from other parts of the country. It is quite fitting that the two-million dollar biology building of West Virginia University, completed in 1951, was named Brooks Hall. This family included nine children of Adolphus and Josephine (Phillips) Brooks. Adolphus Brooks was a teacher in the public schools, a teacher of music, owned and operated a farm, was leader of the choir of the local Presbyterian Church and for forty years superintendent of its Sunday School. Three of his children, Fred, Earl and Alonzo, became widely known for their scientific attainments. They were reared in a community where semi-pioneer conditions still existed. In a Christian home where they were reared they learned the lessons of virtue, industry, kindness, honesty and love.

It might be said that they were born with a love of nature. This tendency was encouraged and developed by their environment, and by their parents. This is illustrated by the following story:[1] "One day in spring, while Fred was still a young boy, his mother went to visit her parents on Mulberry Ridge. When returning home through the woods she came upon a beautiful flower the like of which she had never before seen. She wished to pick the blossoms and take them with her but to do this the plant must be destroyed. So she left it blooming and went on home where she told the children about it. Later she described it minutely to them and asked that they find it for her. For some reason the plant could not be rediscovered, but the search did not stop. For two years, during the spring, he and his brothers searched the woods for this flower. Eventually they found it—the purple-fringed orchid. To the experiences of this search he attributed a distinct stimulus to his love of the woods."

[1]C. R. Cutright, "Fred E. Brooks," *The Pioneer* (*7th report*) 1930. p. 4.

Fred Ernest Brooks was born at French Creek, West Virginia, June 8, 1868. After receiving his training in public country schools, he took a business course in the Academy in Buckhannon. Nature had not fitted him for life in an office and he

Fig. 14. Earl Amos Brooks

Fig. 15. Fred Ernest Brooks

Fig. 16. Alonzo Beecher Brooks

Fig. 17. Chandler Linn Brooks

soon returned to his father's farm. He did not attend college but received excellent training by his untiring efforts in reading, observing and thinking.

In 1896 he married Grace Coburn, of French Creek. Their children were Maurice, Dorothy and Elizabeth.

To his general farming he added the growing of fruits, including strawberries, raspberries and grapes, and later planted orchards of peaches, plums, pears and apples. His success in growing fruit and combating insects led to his appointment as agent and later as associate entomologist of the West Virginia Agricultural Experiment Station. For eight years he served in the capacity as inspector of orchards and nurseries, visiting orchards throughout the State, and giving instructions in the control of insects. He moved his family to Morgantown, but they usually spent most of the summer on the farm at French Creek. He collected extensive data on various insects and small mammals, most of his material being published in bulletins of the Experiment Station. He also contributed articles to the *Rural New Yorker, Country Life in America, The West Virginia Farmer,* and other journals. His bulletins and articles were concise, clear, and interestingly written, and they brought him favorably to the attention of the public. He was called upon to prepare and deliver many addresses.

In 1908 he accepted a position with the United States Bureau of Entomology as associate entomologist in charge of deciduous fruit insect investigations for the Appalachian region, with the condition that his headquarters laboratory be established at French Creek. In this position he worked with many of the same problems that occupied his attention while with the Experiment Station, but his field was much broader. He supervised various projects located from Maine to Michigan and to Georgia and Alabama. Upon his annual visits to many of the places he amassed a large store of knowledge concerning insects and natural science in general. His best known scientific work was with several species of apple tree borers. The results of his investigations, mostly published by the United States Department of Agriculture, are recognized today as the standard source of information concerning these insects. He also conducted important investigations with grape vine root borer, the codling moth, the plum curculio, the walnut husk maggot and different species attacking chestnut, hickory and walnut.[2]

[2]See his list of publications at the end of this biographical sketch.

While working near Washington, D. C., during the summer of 1930, he suffered a heat stroke from which he never fully recovered. In 1931 he retired from his position, and devoted much time writing articles of appeal to the general naturalist. They were published in various magazines, but mostly in *The West Virginia Review*. He was also an accomplished photographer and furnished numerous superb photographs depicting nature that were used as cover scenes for *The West Virginia Review*.

He died on March 9, 1933, at the age of 65, at his home on French Creek. In the issue of April, 1933, *The West Virginia Review* used a fitting last contribution of Fred E. Brooks, entitled "God in Science." In connection with the article J. C. McWhorter gave the following appreciation:[3]

> "In the death of Fred E. Brooks West Virginia has lost one of her finest and most useful citizens. Modest, unassuming, he was, yet, through his writings, addresses and life, a powerful force in bringing to our people a true appreciation of our State and of life at its best.
>
> "A scientist and ardent student of the great outdoors, he, 'in the love of Nature, held communion with her visible forms,' and to him 'she spoke a various language.' The scent of forests, the tint of wild flowers, the tree etchings of lofty skylines, the stately beauty of the wild, the delicate lacery of ferns, the melodies of the woodland, and all the untellable glories of Nature, were to him galleries of divine art and symphonies of heavenly music. They entered his soul and became parts of him, and tenderly drew him close to the heart of the Infinite.
>
> "Of these things—the things that are sweet and pure and lovely—he built within him a spiritual estate that lifted him above the sordid things of life and made him live on a plane above the level of mere THINGS. They made his life rich and sweet, and filled it with a nameless, indescribable joy that radiated from him, inspiring and helping those with whom he mingled. In his soul, 'where moth and rust do not corrupt, and where thieves cannot break through and steal,' by his daily life and thought, he built up a spiritual estate that in times of stress, calamity or financial woe held him serene and trustful and steadfast in the certain knowledge that the things of real value are

[3] J. C. McWhorter, "Fred E. Brooks—An Appreciation," *West Virginia Review* (April, 1933), 204-205.

within, not without—a treasure stored within that cannot be lost, that grows as it is spent, improves as it is used, expands as it is drawn from, and multiplies as it is shared with others. No one could converse with him, hear him speak, or read from his pen, without feeling the uplift of his spirituality dwelling in him.

"Herein was his towering worth to the State. He inspired people, young and old alike, with a deeper appreciation and love of the beautiful within and without. He was a dreamer, as most scientists are—a dreamer of beautiful dreams that were real to his soul and which he made real to others. After all, that is what really survives. From the historyless past to the present the things of mere material wealth have never lived—save, possibly, the barbaric gold buried as a part of barbaric splendor in some Tutenkhamon's tomb. But the dreams live on. The things of art and love alone survive the wrecks of time."

In his honor the West Virginia Academy of Science established in 1935 the Fred E. Brooks Memorial Arboretum, at Watoga State Park. Since 1963 it has been administered in connection with the University Arboretum.

A selected list of his publications of especial interest to botanists are as follows:

Our doomed chestnuts. *W. Va. Review* 1(8):24-25. 1924.

Wild flowers on the French Creek Game Refuge. *W. Va. Wildlife* 2(13):6-7. 1925.

A day afield in southern West Virginia. *W. Va. Review* 3(5):137. 1926.

Some West Virginia wild flowers. *W. Va. Review* 4:204, 286. 1927.

Our beautiful wild azaleas. *W. Va. Review* 7:173, 183. 1930.

West Virginia wild flowers. *W. Va. Review* 7:326-327. 1930.

When autumn comes to the South Branch Valley. *W. Va. Review* 9:112-113. 1931.

Other articles of a more general nature of interest to naturalists are as follows:

Birds of our mountains. *W. Va. Review* 1:11-12. 1924.

The wild gardens. *W. Va. Review* 1:9, 31. 1924.

Things small and great. *W. Va. Review* 2:234, 235, 252, 255. 1925.

West Virginia scientists. *W. Va. Review* 2:308, 345. 1925.

Here and there. *W. Va. Review* 4:175, 184. 1927.

I nominate the tufted titmouse. *W. Va. Review* 5:263. 1928.

Birds with interesting histories. *W. Va. Review* 6:269, 287. 1929.

Sixty-five million thousand-legs. *W. Va. Review* 7:105, 115. 1930.

A little bird told me. *W. Va. Review* 7:139, 155. 1930.

Running away from work. *W. Va. Review* 7:205, 220. 1930.

A sower went forth to sow. *W. Va. Review* 7:235, 254. 1930.

The "Big Road" and the "School Road." *W. Va. Review* 7:355, 371, 372. 1930.

Hymenopterous namesake. *W. Va. Review* 8:190, 191, 212. 1930.

"A numerous company of flies." *W. Va. Review* 8:223, 243. 1931.

Two homes. *W. Va. Review* 8:254-255. 1931.

The far call. *W. Va. Review* 8:322, 323, 350. 1931.

Two master builders. *W. Va. Review* 8:358-359. 1931.

Along our highways. *W. Va. Review* 8:394-395. 1931.

The quarter-mile spring. *W. Va. Review* 9:72, 73, 80. 1931.

"Go to the ant." *W. Va. Review* 9:148, 149, 173. 1931.

I don't like snakes. *W. Va. Review* 9:186-187. 1932.

Nuts to take the place of our vanishing chestnuts. *W. Va. Review* 9:220, 221, 246. 1932.

The flower bed under the maple. *W. Va. Review* 9:259, 283, 284. 1932.

Birds of the wilderness. *W. Va. Review* 9:294, 295, 318. 1932.

Cheer-up—The worst is yet to come. *W. Va. Review* 9:336, 337, 354. 1932.

The game of birds'-nesting. *W. Va. Review* 9:370-371. 1932.

In connection with his work as a member of the Entomological Department of the West Virginia Experiment Station and later as associate entomologist with the United States Department of Agriculture with his station at French Creek he wrote a large number of articles dealing mainly with mammals and insects. A selected list of these publications follows: Mammals of West Virginia; the grapevine root-borer; habits of mice, moles, and shrews; the grape curculio; insects injurious to nuts; the roundheaded appletree borer; the hickory spiral borer; the flatheaded appletree borer; the pear tree borer; the walnut husk maggot; snout beetles that attack nuts; the parandra borer.

Alonzo Beecher Brooks was born at French Creek, May 6, 1873. After attending one-room public schools in 1880-94, he completed a business course at West Virginia Wesleyan College in 1900, and received the bachelor of science degree in agriculture at West Virginia University in 1912.

He married Nellie R. Coburn, sister of Grace Coburn, on June 22, 1899.

Before starting his career as a forester and a naturalist, he was a farmer, a surveyor in 1890-95, and a school teacher for a number of years after 1895. As forester for the West Virginia Geological Survey in 1910-11, he assembled a mass of material, which was published as "Forestry and Wood Industries," a book of 481 pages, issued by the Geological Survey in 1911. He served as forester of the West Virginia Agricultural Experiment Station in 1913-15. He was connected with the West Virginia Department of Agriculture in 1916-17, and was forest pathologist with the United States Department of Agriculture in 1917-21, chief game protector of West Virginia in 1921-28, and naturalist at Oglebay Park, Wheeling, West Virginia from 1928 until his retirement in 1942.

Although he made important contributions to the State while serving as forester and later as game protector, he is perhaps most widely known for his work at Oglebay Park. For many years his Sunday morning "bird walks" attracted hundreds of people from Wheeling and surrounding places. He would bring nature to the level of young and old alike, and the youngsters were made to feel that they were as important as the older folks. He inspired the participants on these walks by quoting from the nature poems of Emerson, Wordsworth, Coleridge and other poets, and influenced many boys and girls to a career in some phase of natural science.

As park naturalist, he was director of the Oglebay Park Nature Training School, which was one of the several features connected with the Oglebay Institute program. The school opened in June, 1928 and lasted for two weeks. Later a camping trip was added, of at first ten days and in 1936 increased to two weeks. During the first two weeks of the course the students lived in comfortable gas-heated, electric-lighted cottages, and took their meals in the camp-center dining room. All classes were held out-of-doors when possible. The second period of the nature training course was devoted more strictly to camp life, the students and staff being transported to some remote mountainous section of West Virginia where they lived in tents, took their meals under a tarpaulin, and led an all-camp life. The study was not confined to botany, but included animals, rocks and stars, beginning on the 750 acre park area and adjacent territory in the Ohio Valley, and ending in the mountains at elevations running to the highest summits in West Virginia. The courses brought students in actual contact with nature, and under the guidance of Mr. Brooks and his staff many persons were stimulated with a desire for further individual field work.

He retired in 1942 and returned to his home at French Creek, and started to rewrite "West Virginia Trees," a book of 242 pages, first issued by the West Virginia Agricultural Experiment Station in 1920. He worked at this until the fall of 1943 when he became critically ill. He died May 16, 1944.

He was a member of the Society of American Foresters, Upper Ohio Valley Historical Society, Phi Beta Kappa, Kappa Alpha, and a charter member of the Southern Appalachian Botanical Club.

It is said of him at Oglebay Park, that "He lives in every tree, every flower, every bird and every scampering furry creature at Oglebay Park, for into the development of Oglebay, as it is today, he poured the richness of his great soul."

A partial list of his publications are as follows:

Description and history of the timber in the Jackson-Mason-Putnam area. *W. Va. Geol. Surv. Co. Repts.* pp. 288-289. 1911.

Forestry and wood industries. *W. Va. Geol. Surv.* Vol. 5. 1911.

Yellow locust in West Virginia. *Problem Report, W. Va. Univ. Coll. Agr.*, Morgantown, W. Va. 1912.

Forests: Doddridge and Harrison Counties. *W. Va. Geol. Surv. Co. Repts.* pp. 653-655. 1912.

Description and history of the timber in the Cabell-Wayne-Lincoln area. *W. Va. Geol. Surv. Co. Repts.* pp. 418-423. 1913.

Present forest conditions, Preston County. *W. Va. Geol. Surv. Co. Repts.* pp. 423-424. 1914.

Forests: Logan and Mingo Counties. *W. Va. Geol. Surv. Co. Repts.* pp. 746-749. 1914.

Forests: Wyoming and McDowell Counties. *W. Va. Geol. Surv. Co. Repts.* pp. 753-758. 1915.

Forests: Lewis and Gilmer Counties. *W. Va. Geol. Surv. Co. Repts.* pp. 612-614. 1916.

Chestnut blight and its control in West Virginia. *1st Biennial Rept., State Crop Pest Comm.* (for years 1913-14). pp. 90-94. 1916.

The chestnut blight and white pine blister rust. *W. Va. Agr. Bull.* 12. 21 pp. 1916.

Forests: Braxton and Clay Counties. *W. Va. Geol. Surv. Co. Repts.* pp. 797-802. 1917.

Forests: Barbour, Upshur and Randolph Counties. *W. Va. Geol. Surv. Co. Repts.* pp. 766-776. 1918.

Forests: Fayette County. *W. Va. Geol. Surv. Co. Repts.* pp. 922-924. 1919.

Forests: Webster County. *W. Va. Geol. Surv. Co. Repts.* pp. 531-533. 1920.

West Virginia trees. *W. Va. Agr. Expt. Sta. Bull.* 175. 242 pp. Illus. 1920. (reissued 1951).

Forests: Nicholas County. *W. Va. Geol. Surv. Co. Repts.* pp. 738-741. 1921.

Forests: Mineral and Grant Counties. *W. Va. Geol. Surv. Co. Repts.* pp. 709-711. 1924.

A new tree for West Virginia. Illus. *W. Va. Wildlife* 3(3):15, 17. 1925.

Forests: Monroe, Mercer and Summers Counties. *W. Va. Geol. Surv. Co. Repts.* pp. 778-782. 1926.

A new tree for West Virginia. Illus. *W. Va. Review* 3:207. 1926.

Evergreens. Illus. *W. Va. Wildlife* 3(8):18-19. 1926.

Hickory, the kinds and uses. Illus. *W. Va. Wildlife* 3(10):17. 1926.

The family of maples. Illus. *W. Va. Wildlife* 3(11):10-11. 1926.

Our oaks. Illus. *W. Va. Wildlife* 3(9):16-17. 1926.

Chestnut and chestnut blight. *W. Va. Wildlife* 5:18-19. 1927.

Holly and mistletoe. Illus. *W. Va. Wildlife* 5(8):24, 34. 1927.

Rhododendron. Illus. *W. Va. Wildlife* 5(3):12-13. 1927.

The famous ginseng and other root plants. Illus. *W. Va. Wildlife* 5(4):16-17. 1927.

Two poisonous plants. Illus. *W. Va. Wildlife* 5(5):14-15. 1927.

Forests: Pocahontas County: Cranberry Glades, modern flora, destructive fungi, native trees. *W. Va. Geol. Surv. Co. Repts.* pp. 348-364. 1929.

Cranberry Glades. *In, The West Virginia Encyclopedia,* W. Va. Publ. Co., Charleston, pp. 185-186. 1929.

Trees of West Virginia. *In, The West Virginia Encyclopedia,* W. Va. Publ. Co., Charleston, pp. 903-914. 1929.

The war of the cedars. *Am. Forests and Forest Life* 36:325-329. 1930.

West Virginia orchids. *W. Va. Wildlife* 10(7-8):2, 11. 1932.

The earliest spring flowers. *W. Va. Review* 13:171. 1936.

A new holly for West Virginia. *J. So. Appalach. Bot. Club* (now *Castanea*) 1:83-85. 1936.

Castanea dentata. Castanea 2:60-66. 1937.

Earl Amos Brooks was born at French Creek, April 20, 1871. He received the bachelor of arts degree at West Virginia University in 1891, and the bachelor's degree in theology at Western Theological Seminary in 1900. He was awarded the honorary degree of doctor of divinity at Davis and Elkins College in 1916. He was a minister in the Presbyterian Church, and served as pastor at Waverly, West Virginia, in 1902-06, Weston, West Virginia, in 1906-16, and at Everett, Massachusetts, in 1916-29. Dr. Brooks served as associate professor in the biology department at Boston University in 1929-41, and associate professor emeritus after 1941. He died April 4, 1952.

Although he was a minister and educator by profession, he was also a naturalist, being especially interested in birds, and also in plants that afford food for birds. He made several collecting trips to the Southern Appalachian region from 1900 to 1916. He was the author of "Game Birds of West Virginia," "The Food of West Virginia Birds," "Forty Common Birds of West Virginia," "Handbook of the Outdoors," and numerous shorter publications dealing with nature lore.

He was a member of the American Ornithologists' Union, and the Nuttall Ornithological Club.

Maurice Graham Brooks, son of Fred E. and Grace Coburn Brooks, was born at French Creek, West Virginia, June 16, 1900. After receiving his grade school and high school training in the schools of Upshur County, he attended West Virginia University, receiving the bachelor of arts degree in 1923 and the master of science degree in 1934. He did graduate work at Michigan State University in 1928 and at the University of Michigan in 1939-41. He was Assistant State 4-H Club Agent of West Virginia in 1923-26, and assistant principal of Upshur County High School in 1926-33. Since 1934 he has been a member of the staff of West Virginia University, serving as instructor of biology in 1934-38, assistant professor of recreational forestry in 1938-42, associate professor of Wildlife Management in 1942-47, professor of Wildlife Management since 1947, and also as forester of the West Virginia Agricultural Experiment Station. During summer sessions he has taught at the University of Virginia and the University of Minnesota. He was chairman of the West Virginia Biological Survey in 1938-46. He also has served as director of the West Virginia Conservation School, and from 1945-53 was a member of the West Virginia Conservation Commission.

He is a fellow in the American Association for Advancement of Science, fellow of the American Ornithologists' Union, Wilson Ornithological Club (president, 1950-52), Wildlife Society, Society of American Foresters, Virginia Society of Ornithology, and the Society of Ichthyologists and Herpetologists.

He has made numerous collecting trips in the State, gathering particularly ferns and orchids. His specimens are filed in the University Herbarium. He also has contributed specimens to the Smithsonian Institution and Michigan State University.

A partial list of his publications relating to botany follows:

Climbing fern found in Upshur County. *Am. Fern Jour.* 15:47-52. 1925.

Asplenium gravesii in West Virginia. *Am. Fern Jour.* 16:97-98. 1926.

West Virginia's orchid wealth. *W. Va. Review* 11:166-168. 1934.

Spring comes to the New River Gorge. *W. Va. Review* 11:198-199. 1934.

Listera cordata (L.) R. Br. found in West Virginia. *Jour. So. Appalach. Bot. Club* (now *Castanea*) 1:15-17. 1936.

Floral arrangement in *Spiranthes gracilis* (Bigel.) Beck. *Castanea* 2:99-100. 1937.

Recent range extensions of two ferns in West Virginia. *Am. Fern Jour.* 30:136. 1940.

A new form of *Ilex longipes* Chapman. *Castanea* 5:15-16. 1940.

Cranberry Glades—fact and fancy. *W. Va. Review* 21:14-16, 27-28. 1944.

The muskeg farthest south. *Audubon Mag.* 47:216-223. 1945.

A new variety of Christmas fern. *Castanea* 12:24-25. 1947.

Effects of black walnut trees and their products on other vegetation. *W. Va. Agr. Expt. Sta. Bull.* 347. 31 pp. 1951.

Ferns associated with black walnut trees. *Am. Fern Jour.* 42:124-130. 1952.

Canaan Valley. *W. Va. Conservation* 21(5):7-10. 1957.

(With A. S. Margolin) The pteridophytes of West Virginia. *W. Va. University Studies* 2. *W. Va. Univ. Bull. Ser.* 39(2):1-60. 1938.

Other publications of a more general nature include the following:

A nature study center. *W. Va. Review* 11:140-141. 1934.

Oglebay Park Nature Training School. *W. Va. Review* 11:234-235. 1934.

Birds of Cheat Mountain. *The Cardinal* 6(2):25-44. 1943.

Oglebay Park—recreation and education. *W. Va. Review* 13:4-7. 1946.

Watoga on the Greenbrier. *W. Va. Review* 13:4-8. 1946.

Maurice Brooks, as a member of the second generation of the Brooks Family, has well upheld the family's reputation as a naturalist.

REFERENCES

BARTHOLOMEW, ELIZABETH ANN. "A. B. Brooks," *Castanea* 9:117-118. 1944.

BROOKS, A. B. "The Oglebay Park Nature Training School," *Castanea* 1:45-48. 1936.

CALLAHAN, JAMES M. "History of West Virginia." Volume III. Chicago and New York: American Historical Society, 1923.

CATTELL, JAQUES. "American Men of Science." (7th ed.) Lancaster: The Science Press, 1944. (8th ed.), 1949.

CATTELL, JAQUES. "American Men of Science." (10th ed.) Arizona State University, Tempe, Arizona: Cattell Press, Inc., 1960.

CORE, EARL L. "Outlines of the Flora of West Virginia." Morgantown: West Virginia University Bookstore, 1954.

CORE, EARL L. "Plant Life of West Virginia." New York: Scholar's Library, 1960.

CORE, EARL L., WILLIAM H. AND BETTY J. GILLESPIE. "Bibliography of the Plant Life of West Virginia." New York: Scholar's Library, 1962.

CUTRIGHT, C. R. "Fred E. Brooks," *The Pioneer*: Seventh Annual Report of the Descendants of French Creek Pioneers (August, 1930), 4.

MCWHORTER, J. C. "Fred E. Brooks—An Appreciation," *West Virginia Review* (April, 1933), 204-205.

CHAPTER X

West Virginia University

As pointed out in Chapter II, botany has been a course of instruction at West Virginia University from the very opening session, in 1867. For the first third of a century, however, courses and students were relatively few and botanical instruction formed only a part-time activity of science teachers. Gradually more courses were added and in 1897-98 a veritable revolution was made in the botany curriculum. Seven botany courses were offered in contrast to the two given for many years. These were Biology 1, Elementary Physiology; Biology 2, Elementary Botany; Biology 3, General Biology; Biology 4, Descriptive Botany; Biology 5, Field Botany; Biology 6, Structural Botany; Biology 13, Bacteriology; and Biology 15. Plant Evolution, Biology 3 and Biology 15, however, were offered as summer courses in 1898.

Improvement in botanical teaching came about in 1899-1900 when **Edwin Bingham Copeland** (1873-1964) was appointed assistant professor of botany. He was born at Monroe, Wisconsin, September 30, 1873. He received the bachelor of arts degree from Leland Stanford University in 1895 and the master of arts degree and doctor of philosophy degree from the University of Halle, Germany in 1896. He also studied at the University of Leipzig, Germany in 1895-96, at the University of Wisconsin in 1896-97, 1898, and at the University of Chicago in 1900-01. After serving as assistant in biology at the University of Wisconsin in 1893-94 and as honorary fellow in botany in 1896-97, he served as assistant professor of botany at Indiana University in 1897-98, and as teacher of science in the State Normal School at Chico, California, in 1899.

Botany was established as a separate department in 1899-1900, and Dr. Copeland set up the following curriculum:

Botany 1. Elementary Botany—Fall; Botany 2. Elementary Field Botany—Summer, Spring; Botany 3. The Algae—Fall; Botany 4. Fungi and Bryophytes—Winter; Botany 5. Vascular Plants—Spring; Botany 6. The Epidermal and Fundamental

Fig. 18. Brooks Hall. The biology building at West Virginia University. ▷

Tissues—Fall; Botany 7. The Fibrovascular System—Winter; Botany 8. Cytology—Spring; Botany 9. Physical Physiology; Botany 10. Chemical Physiology—Fall; Botany 11. Growth and Irritability—Spring; Botany 13. Teacher Course—Summer; Botany 15. Lectures on Physiology—Winter; Botany 16. Local Ecology — Summer; Botany 17. Cryptogamic Short Course—Summer; Botany 20. Research.

During the 1900-01 term, his last year at the University, Dr. Copeland offered about the same courses. He was instructor in botany at Stanford University, 1901-03, and thereafter spent many years in the Philippine Islands. He died March 16, 1964.

In 1901-02 the Botany Department was combined with the Zoology Department to form the Department of Biology. Dr. **Kary Cadmus Davis** served for one year as professor of horticulture at the Agricultural Experiment Station, and as instructor of botany at the University. He attended Kansas State College, receiving the bachelor of science degree in 1892 and the master of science degree in 1894. He served for six years as principal of the high school in Austin, Minnesota, and received the doctor of philosophy degree from Cornell University in 1900. Before joining the staff at the University, he served for one year as professor of botany in the State Normal School, St. Cloud, Minnesota. During the one year that Dr. Davis served at the University the botany curriculum was reduced to the following six courses:

Botany 2. Ecology of Fall Plants—Fall; Botany 3. Ecology of Spring Plants—Spring; Botany 4. Cytology of Simple Tissues—Winter; Botany 5. Tissue Systems—Winter; Botany 6. Plant Reproduction—Fall; Botany 7. Plant Physiology—Winter.

Botany was a separate department in 1902-03, and **William Montgomery Morgan** served as instructor of botany, in addition to his duties as assistant horticulturist. He received his bachelor of science degree in agriculture from Cornell University in 1902. In addition to the courses that were offered the previous year, he taught a course in Economic Botany in the Department of Agriculture, and introduced an Introductory Botany course in the Botany Department during the summer session of 1903.

Mr. Morgan died unexpectedly during the 1903 summer session, being replaced by **Thomas C. Johnson**, who served from 1902 to 1907 as instructor in botany, and assistant horticulturist. He attended West Virginia University, receiving the bachelor of science degree in 1896 and the master of arts degree in 1901. He served as instructor in science at Lee Military Academy in 1896-99, fellow and graduate student at West Virginia University in 1899-1901, acting professor of horticulture at the University of Missouri in 1901-02, and a fellow in horticulture at Cornell University in 1902-03.

In 1903-04 the Botany Department courses were moved from University Hall (now Woodburn Hall) to the Agricultural Experiment Station. Mr. Johnson set up the following curriculum:

Botany 1. Elementary Botany—Winter; Botany 2. Elementary Botany—Spring; Botany 3. General Botany—Fall; Botany 4. General Botany—Winter; Botany 5. General Botany—Spring; Botany 6. Systematic Botany of the Vascular Plants—Fall, Winter, Spring; Botany 7. Plant Physiology—Fall.

In 1905-07 the Botany Department offered only three courses as follows:

Botany 1. General Botany—Fall; Botany 2. General Botany—Winter; Botany 3. Systematic Botany of Vascular Plants—Spring.

For this two year period, in his course listings in the University Catalogue, Mr. Johnson called attention to related courses offered in the Department of Plant Pathology and also those offered by Professor John L. Sheldon in the Department of Bacteriology.

During the summer session of 1906 two courses in Nature Study were introduced, one being taught by **Mr. Wilbur S. Jackman** of the University of Chicago and the other by Dr. Sheldon. The courses were non-technical, consisting of daily lectures on selected topics. Some of the topics were, Nature Study for Everybody; Along the Fence Rows; West Virginia Hills; A Bunch of Spring Beauties; Clouds and Sunshine; and Morning and Evening Walks. Mr. Johnson offered four courses during the 1907 summer session under the instructional heading of Agriculture, Botany and Horticulture. The classes were held, for the first time, in Martin Hall.

A significant development came about in 1907-08 when the Departments of Botany and Bacteriology were combined, headed by Dr. Sheldon. The Department was moved from Martin Hall to North Fife Cottage, one of the two buildings of wooden construction, built in 1903, near the present Cafeteria. In addition to three courses in bacteriology, he offered Elementary Botany and General Botany during the Fall term, followed by a continuation during the Winter term; Elementary Plant Physiology and Pathology during the Spring term; and Systematic Botany of Vascular Plants and also Advanced Plant Physiology and Pathology by appointment. Improvements were also made in the Summer session curriculum. Six courses were offered as follows: Elementary Agriculture; Botany; Nature Study; Agricultural Nature Study; Elementary Agriculture; and Agriculture for Secondary Schools.

The course offerings remained about the same until the 1912-13 term, when two semesters replaced three quarters and Summer School was extended from six to nine weeks. Courses offered were:

Botany 1. General Botany—First Semester; Botany 2. General Botany—Second Semester; Botany 5. Systematic Botany of Seed Plants—Second Semester; Botany 6. Systematic Botany of Seed Plants—First Semester; Botany 12. Plant Physiology—First Semester; Botany 13. Plant Physiology—Second Semester; Botany 14. Plant Pathology—First Semester; Botany 15. Plant Pathology—Second Semester; Botany 17. Advanced Plant Pathology—Throughout Year; Botany 18. Histology—First and Second Semesters; hours arranged.

Botany 1 and 2 were prerequisites for all courses in botany. Advanced students were permitted to consult the Herbarium of the Experiment Station and Professor Sheldon's private herbarium. A reading knowledge of one or more of the following languages was considered desirable: Latin, German and French.

In 1913-14 Dr. Sheldon received some assistance, when **Edward Fred Woodcock** was appointed as instructor of botany. He was born in Pittsford, Vermont, February 13, 1885. After receiving the bachelor of science degree from the University of Vermont in 1909, he attended Yale University, receiving the degree of master of arts in 1912 and the degree of doctor of philosophy in 1917. He was head of the Biology Department at Juniata College in 1909-10.

In 1913-14, with the assistance of Mr. Woodcock, Dr. Sheldon added the following new courses:

Botany 3. Agricultural Botany—First Semester; Botany 4. Agricultural Botany—Second Semester; Botany 10. General Bacteriology—First and Second Semester; Botany 20. Botanical Technique—First and Second Semesters; Botany 21. Methods of Teaching Botany—Second Semester.

After serving for one year Mr. Woodcock left the University, and Robert Clifton Spangler[1] and Ivan D. Shunk were added to the botany staff.

Ivan D. Shunk was born February 6, 1891, in Sherrodsville, Ohio, and reared for a period of his boyhood in Canada. He received his bachelor's degree from West Virginia University in 1913, and was a member of Phi Beta Kappa. He served as student assistant in the Botany Department in 1914-16 and as instructor in 1916-17. After an interim of graduate study at the University of Chicago, he joined the staff of North Carolina State College in 1919, where he made an enviable record. He received the doctor of philosophy degree at Rutgers University in 1928. Dr. Shunk died on July 11, 1951.

From 1913 until his retirement in 1919, Dr. Sheldon offered about the same courses, except for the addition of Botany 3, General Botany and Botany 4, Seed Plants, in 1917.

In 1915 the legislature appropriated $100,000 for an agricultural building; this was completed in 1918 and named Oglebay Hall in honor of E. W. Oglebay. The Botany Department was moved from the inadequate North Fife Cottage to the top floor of Oglebay Hall for the term of 1919-20. Dr. Sheldon left the University on October 1, 1919, and was replaced by Harlan Harvey York.

Harlan Harvey York was born at Plainfield, Indiana, September 8, 1875. After receiving the bachelor of science degree at DePauw University in 1903, he was an assistant in the Botany Department of Ohio State University in 1903-05, receiving the master of arts degree in 1905. He received the doctor of philosophy degree at Johns Hopkins University in 1911. Before joining the faculty of West Virginia University, he served as instructor of botany at the University of Texas in 1906-09, and as associate professor, in charge of the Botany Department at Brown University in 1911-19. After leaving the University in 1923, he served as forest pathologist with the United States Department of Agriculture and as forest pathologist with the Conservation Commission, Albany, New York from 1923 until 1929. After 1929 until he retired, he served as collaborator with the Bureau of Plant Industry, United States Department of Agriculture; professor of botany at the University of Pennsylvania; and pathologist at the Morris Arboretum.

During Dr. York's tenure Mr. Spangler was advanced to assistant professor, Eva Myrtelle (Fling) Roush, who had served

[1]See p. 122.

as graduate assistant, was advanced to instructor, and Nelle Perrel Ammons[2] and Morris Abel Raines were added to the staff as instructors.

Eva Myrtelle Fling was born at Tanner, West Virginia. She attended West Virginia University, receiving the bachelor of arts degree in 1911 and the master of arts degree in 1920. After serving as a high school teacher in 1911-17, she served in the Botany Department as an assistant in 1917-20 and instructor in 1920-24. While working on her master's degree in 1918, Miss Fling made a systematic study of the algae of West Virginia, in the localities of Morgantown, Glenville, and Tanner. Her collection served as a basis for her master's thesis ("One hundred algae of West Virginia," *Castanea* 4:11-26. 1939). After leaving the University she served in the Botany Department of Franklin College, in Indiana, as instructor and then assistant professor. In 1930 she received the doctor of philosophy degree from Washington University in St. Louis. Then she continued her work in botany at the Herbarium of the Missouri Botanical Gardens, and later at the Arnold Arboretum of Harvard University.

Morris Abel Raines was born in Latvia, March 31, 1894, and was naturalized in 1951. He attended Columbia University, receiving the bachelor of science degree in 1915, the master of arts degree in 1917, and the doctor of philosophy degree in botany in 1922. He was an assistant in botany at Columbia University in 1916-17, science assistant in physiology with the United States Public Health Service in 1917, and botany instructor at West Virginia University in 1920-21. After leaving the University he served as assistant professor and later as associate professor of botany at Howard University in 1930-39, and professor at the same institution after 1939.

The courses and staff remained the same in 1921-22. Mr. Raines left the staff at the end of his term, and Dr. York left at the end of the 1922-23 term, and was replaced by Perry Daniel Strausbaugh. This was an important year in the development of botany at the University, as significant changes were made in the curriculum, which was gradually evolving into the present up-to-date program. The curriculum was set up as follows:

Botany 1. General Botany; Botany 2. General Botany (continuation of Botany 1); Botany 5. Systematic Botany; Botany

[2]See p. 121.

6. Pharmaceutical Botany; Botany 10. Bacteriology; Botany 12. Plant Physiology; Botany 16. Advanced Plant Physiology; Botany 22. Morphology and Phylogeny; Botany 23. Morphology and Phylogeny (continuation of Botany 22); Botany 31. History of Botany; Botany 32. Plant Ecology; Botany 33. Forest Ecology; Botany 34. Experimental Ecology; Botany 35. Microtechnique and Plant Histology; Botany 36. Botany Seminar; Botany 37. Botany Seminar (continuation of Botany 36).

The University Catalogue also stated: "Special courses will be offered for students desiring to pursue graduate work in botany. Such students should consult the head of the department concerning the nature and content of these courses."

In 1924 Mrs. Roush left the department and Joseph Banks Rhine and Bertram Donald Barclay were added as instructors.

Joseph Banks Rhine was born in Waterloo, Pennsylvania, September 29, 1895. He attended the University of Chicago, receiving the bachelor of science degree in 1922, the master of science degree in 1923, and the doctor of philosophy degree in botany in 1925. After serving as instructor in botany (teaching courses in physiology) at West Virginia University in 1924-26, he studied at Harvard University in 1926-27; he served at Duke University as a fellow in 1927-28, instructor in philosophy and psychology in 1928-29, assistant professor of psychology in 1929-35, associate professor in 1935-37, professor in 1937-40, and became director of the parapsychology laboratory in 1940. Here he became internationally known as a proponent of the concept of extra-sensory perception (ESP).

Bertram Donald Barclay was born on November 9, 1898, in Champaign, Illinois. He received the bachelor of science degree from Wooster College in 1923, attended Syracuse University in 1923-24, received the degree of master of science from West Virginia University in 1926, and the doctor of philosophy degree in botany from the University of Chicago in 1928. After serving as instructor of botany at West Virginia University in 1924-26, he became a botany professor at the University of Tulsa, starting in 1928. He died June 6, 1953, as the result of injuries sustained in an automobile accident on the preceding day.

The staff and courses offered were the same in 1925-26. Dr. Rhine and Mr. Barclay left at the end of the term, and Dr. Spangler was advanced to professor. Herbert Snow Wolfe was appointed assistant professor, succeeding Dr. Rhine as physiologist.

Herbert Snow Wolfe was born at Parkville, Missouri, September 14, 1898. He received the bachelor of arts degree at Park College in 1918. He attended the University of Chicago, receiving the master of science degree in 1926 and the doctor of philosophy degree in 1930. He served as a high school teacher in Missouri in 1918-19; instructor of science at Westminster College (Utah) in 1919-20; assistant professor of botany at the University of Kentucky in 1921-24; assistant in plant physiology at the University of Chicago in 1924-26; assistant professor of botany at West Virginia University in 1926-29; associate horticulturist at Experiment Station, Florida, 1930-32, horticulturist in charge in 1932-38, and professor of horticulture and head of the department at the University of Florida in 1938.

The staff and courses remained the same in 1927-28, but the department was moved from Oglebay Hall to Science Hall, which had been completely renovated following the removal of the Chemistry Department to the new Chemistry Building. The Zoology Department, under Dr. A. M. Reese, was moved from Woodburn Hall and Botany and Zoology, as separate departments, occupied Science Hall jointly.

Earl Lemley Core was appointed as instructor in botany in 1928 and Ward McClintic Sharp served on the staff as instructor in 1931-32, while Mr. Core was at Columbia University working on his doctorate.

Ward McClintic Sharp was born at Fairview, West Virginia, November 2, 1904. He attended West Virginia University, receiving the bachelor of arts degree in 1931 and the master of science degree in 1932. In 1934 he received the doctor of philosophy degree from Washington University in St. Louis.

He was instructor in the Department of Botany at West Virginia University in 1931-32, and student assistant at Washington University in 1932-34. Dr. Sharp has served as Education Supervisor in the U. S. Office of Education in 1934-35, assistant biologist in the Migratory Waterfowl Division of the U. S. Fish and Wildlife Service in 1935-48, and biologist and leader, Pennsylvania Co-operative Wildlife Unit since 1948. He is a member of the Ecological Society of America, Wildlife Society, Society of Mammalogists, and the Wilson Ornithological Society.

While a student at West Virginia University from 1928 to 1931, he made a careful study of the Compositae of the state. His collection of 136 sheets representing typical forms are in the University Herbarium (See also his "Pore fungi of Monongalia County." *Proc. W. Va. Acad. Sci.* 6:29-31. 1933).

Botany, Zoology, and Plant Pathology were combined in 1933 into the Department of Biology (in the College of Agriculture), with C. R. Orton, of Plant Pathology, as head. This arrangement continued until 1936, when Botany and Zoology were returned to the College of Arts and Sciences as a new Department of Biology, under Dr. Reese. Dr. Strausbaugh succeeded Dr. Reese as head of the Department in 1937.

Genevieve Clulo (Berg) was added to the staff in 1934. She was born at Bellaire, Ohio, January 29, 1905. She attended West Virginia University, receiving the bachelor of arts degree in 1928 and the master of arts degree in 1929. She attended the University of Chicago from June, 1929 to September, 1930, and again during the summer of 1936. After serving in the botany department as graduate assistant in 1934-35, she joined the plant pathology department as instructor, where she remained until her retirement on July 1, 1952. At this time she was associate plant pathologist and associate professor of plant pathology. She held membership in the American Phytopathology Society, American Association for Advancement of Science, Southern Appalachian Botanical Club, Torrey Botanical Club, West Virginia Academy of Science, Phi Beta Kappa, Sigma Delta Epsilon (honorary science society for women), and Phi Epsilon Phi. Her publications and those with her husband, Anthony Berg, deal mainly with internal bark necrosis of apples. She died October 20, 1955.

Donald Dirk Ritchie was added to the staff in 1938, teaching plant physiology. He was born on March 28, 1914, in Atlanta, Georgia. He attended Furman University, receiving the bachelor of arts degree in 1933 and the bachelor of science degree in 1944. He attended the University of Virginia during the summers of 1934, 1935, 1936, 1939, and 1941. He attended the University of North Carolina, receiving the master of arts degree in 1937 and the doctor of philosophy degree in botany in 1947. At Furman University he served as assistant in biology in 1933-34 and instructor in 1934-35. He was assistant in botany at the University of North Carolina in 1935-38. After serving as instructor in biology at West Virginia University in 1938-42, he served in the United States Marines in 1942-46, and returned to the University as assistant professor of biology. In this capacity he taught most of the plant physiology courses in 1946-48. After leaving the University he served at Barnard College, Columbia University, as associate professor in 1948-54, professor since 1954, and head of the department since 1951.

He has also served as mycologist in the Naval Research Laboratory in 1948 and director of the National Naval Research Laboratory, Exposure Station, Panama, in 1953-54. He is a member of the Mycological Society of America, Society of Industrial Microbiologists, Botanical Society of America, Torrey Botanical Club, and Southern Appalachian Botanical Club.

Dr. Strausbaugh retired in 1948 and Dr. Core was made head of the department. Charles Henry Baer and Herald Durward Bennett joined the staff the same year.

Charles Henry Baer was born at Columbus, Ohio, September 1, 1919. He attended Ohio State University, receiving the bachelor of science degree in 1947 and the master of arts degree in 1948. He received the doctor of philosophy degree from the University of Maryland in 1961. After serving in the United States Army in 1941-45, he has served in the Biology Department of West Virginia University, as instructor in plant physiology and ecology in 1948-61 and as assistant professor since 1961. His research has been in his fields of specialization, dealing with plant water relations, physiological instrumentation, microclimatology, indicator species, and forest ecology. He is a member of the Society of Plant Physiologists.

Herald Durward Bennett (Fig. 20) was born in Akron, Ohio, June 17, 1916. He received the degrees of bachelor of arts (1940) and master of arts (1941) at West Virginia University, and the doctor of philosophy degree at the State University of Iowa (1949). He joined the biology staff of West Virginia University as instructor in 1948, becoming assistant professor in 1953, associate professor in 1955, and professor in 1961.

He is a member of Sigma Xi, Botanical Society of America, Iowa Academy of Science, Southern Appalachian Botanical Club (associate editor), West Virginia Academy of Science (president, 1961-62), and others. He is very active in civic and public affairs and is a member of the Morgantown Kiwanis Club (president, 1960), of the First Christian Church of Morgantown (chairman of the official board), and other organizations. He is president of the Monongalia Rest Home Corporation and Sundale Rest Home Board and is a colonel in the United States Army Reserve.

Dr. Bennett teaches morphology, and for a number of years was in charge of the field courses in botany offered during the summer sessions at the University Biological Station at Camp Wood, succeeding the old Biological Expeditions. Upon the establishment of the Terra Alta Biological Station in 1962 he became its first director. He is intensely interested in the study of algae and has made important contributions in that field.

Fig. 19. Nelle Perrell Ammons

Fig. 20. Herald Durward Bennett

Fig. 21. Frank Albert Gilbert

Fig. 22. Robert Clifton Spangler

(See his "Algae of West Virginia; Mesotaeniaceae and Desmidiaceae." *Castanea* 25:96-101. 1960.)

William Thomas Jackson joined the botany staff in 1949-50, replacing Mr. Baer for one year. He was born in Stockdale, Ohio, May 10, 1923. He received the bachelor of science degree from Ohio State University in 1947, the master of science degree from the University of Tennessee in 1949, and the doctor of philosophy degree in botany from Duke University in 1953. He was an assistant in botany at the University of Tennessee 1947-49 and instructor in biology and plant physiology at the University in 1949-50. Since leaving the University staff in 1950, he served as assistant in botany at Duke University in 1950-52 and research assistant in 1953; associate professor at Clemson College in 1952; and Instructor at the Osborn Botany Laboratory, Yale University, in 1953-57 and assistant professor in 1957-59; and since 1959 has been professor of botany at Dartmouth College.

Genevieve Poland Smell was added to the staff in 1946 and **Ellen Zink Vandervort** in 1949. Mrs. Smell died January 23, 1960. Her work was chiefly in general biology.

Ellen Zink Vandervort was born August 28, 1910 in Murdock, Nebraska. She graduated from Peru State Teachers College in 1932 with the bachelor of arts degree. She received her master of science degree from the University of Nebraska in 1943 in botany, and also had two and one-half years of additional work in botany at that institution. Later she took more graduate work in botany at West Virginia University.

She taught for eight years in high school in Nebraska. She was a graduate assistant for three years and assistant instructor one year at the University of Nebraska. She was a teaching fellow in the Biology Department at West Virginia University while doing graduate work, and then served for seven more years as an instructor. She worked part-time as a seed analyst at the University of Nebraska, and for ten months as seed analyst for Colorado State University. She has been teaching in the high school at Morenci, Arizona, since 1957.

She is a member of Sigma Xi, Beta Beta Beta, Sigma Tau Delta, Kappa Delta Pi, Phi Epsilon Phi, Sigma Delta Epsilon, Delta Kappa Gamma, Southern Appalachian Botanical Club, Pythian Sisters, Eastern Star, St. James Episcopal Guild, Girl Scouts, and Morenci Teachers Association. She has contributed a number of specimens to the herbarium of West Virginia University.

Mason E. Hale, Jr. joined the staff in 1955. He was born September 23, 1928 in Winsted, Conn. He received the bachelor of science degree from Yale University in 1950 and the doctor of philosophy degree from the University of Wisconsin in 1953. He was assistant professor at the University of Wichita, 1953-55, assistant professor at West Virginia University, 1955-57, and since 1957 curator, Division of Cryptogams, Smithsonian Institution. Dr. Hale is an authority on lichens and has developed an international reputation. He wrote the "Lichen Handbook," a text of 178 pages, published by the Smithsonian Institution in 1961. He has written dozens of articles in scientific journals dealing with his specialty.

He is a member of the American Society of Plant Taxonomists, Bryological Society of America, and the Southern Appalachian Botanical Club. Dr. Hale collected 11,000 specimens of lichens, including 2,500 from West Virginia, from 1952-1959, depositing them in the Smithsonian Herbarium.

Mrs. Vandervort and Dr. Hale left the department in 1957, and Jesse F. Clovis and Roy B. Clarkson succeeded them.

Jesse F. Clovis was born at Clarksburg, West Virginia, January 31, 1921. He attended West Virginia University, receiving the bachelor of science degree in forestry in 1947 and the master of science degree in botany in 1952. He received the doctor of philosophy degree from Cornell University in 1955.

He served on the botany staff of the University of Connecticut in 1955-57, and in 1957 joined the staff of the department of biology of West Virginia University as assistant professor, becoming associate professor in 1962. He has been teaching systematic botany and general biology, in addition to the National Science Foundation Summer Institute courses.

Dr. Clovis is a member of the American Association for Advancement of Science, Sigma Xi (president, WVU Chapter, 1963), American Institute of Biological Sciences, Southern Appalachian Botanical Club (book review editor, *Castanea*), West Virginia Academy of Science, and the American Society of Plant Taxonomists.

His collection of plants from central New York was given to the University Herbarium in 1953. (See his, "The altitudinal distribution of wildlife plant food shrubs in West Virginia." *M.S. thesis, W. Va. Univ. Graduate School,* Morgantown, W. Va. 1952, and "A note about Oxydendrum" *Castanea* 24:51-52. 1959.)

Roy Burdette Clarkson, son of Walter George and Mertie Curry Clarkson, was born at Cass, West Virginia, October 25, 1926. He graduated from Green Bank High School in 1944, and received the bachelor of science degree at Davis and Elkins College in 1951. He attended West Virginia University, receiving the master of science degree in 1953 and the doctor of philosophy degree in 1960. He taught at Green Bank High School in 1951-52, Suncrest Junior High, Morgantown, West Virginia in 1952-56, and has served on the staff of the Biology Department of the University, as instructor in 1956-60, and as assistant professor since 1960.

Dr. Clarkson is a member of the American Society of Plant Taxonomists, Southern Appalachian Botanical Club (treasurer since 1959), Association of Southeastern Biologists, West Virginia Academy of Science, Society of the Sigma Xi, and the Spruce Street Methodist Church.

He made a thorough study of the Monongahela National Forest from 1951 to 1959, collecting approximately 4,000 specimens, which he deposited in the herbarium of West Virginia University. (See his: The vascular flora of the Monongahela National Forest. *Diss., W. Va. Univ. Graduate School*, Morgantown, W. Va. 1960.) Other publications include the following: A range extension for *Saxifraga pensylvanica. Castanea* 20:131. 1955; Blister Swamp, West Virginia. *Castanea* 22:137-138. 1957; The genus *Robinia* in West Virginia. *Castanea* 23:56-58. 1958; Twinflower in West Virginia. *Castanea* 23:110. 1958; Scotch heather in North America. *Castanea* 23:119-130. 1958; The West Virginia *Spiraea. Castanea* 24:143-146. 1959; Notes on the distribution of *Alnus crispa* in eastern North America. *Castanea* 25:83-86. 1960; *Scheuchzeria palustris* L. var. *americana. Castanea* 26:102-103. 1961; The return of a native, *Spiraea virginiana. Arboretum Newsletter.* Aug. 1960; (with Hutton, Eugene E.) Two plants new for North America and some new or otherwise interesting plants in West Virginia. *Castanea* 26:84-88. 1961; and Fraser's Sedge, *Cymophyllus fraseri* (Andrews) Mackenzie. *Castanea* 26:129-136. 1961.

Dr. Ammons retired at the end of the 1958-59 term, and was replaced by Dr. R. J. Tolbert.

Robert John Tolbert was born at Pelican Rapids, Minnesota, April 16, 1928. He served as first lieutenant in the United States Air Force in 1948-53. After receiving the degrees of bachelor of science and bachelor of arts at Moorhead State Teachers College, Moorhead, Minnesota, in 1955, he attended

Rutgers University, receiving the doctor of philosophy degree in botany in 1959.

Dr. Tolbert served on the staff of the Biology Department of West Virginia University as assistant professor from 1959 to 1962 and as associate professor in 1962-63, in the fields of his specialization, plant anatomy and morphology. He has done considerable research dealing with the shoot apex in certain angiosperms. He developed a new technique of block staining of paraffin mounts, which has received international acclaim. (See his "Block staining of botanical materials." *Stain Technology* 37:165-169. 1962.) He resigned in 1963 to accept a position on the staff of Moorhead College.

In 1960-61 Mr. Baer took a leave-of-absence to complete his doctor's degree at the University of Maryland, and was replaced for the year by Dr. J. J. Dyar.

James Joseph Dyar was born at Marietta, Ohio, November 1, 1931. He attended West Virginia University, receiving the bachelor of arts degree in 1954 and the master of science degree in 1957. He received the doctor of philosophy degree from Ohio State University in 1960.

Nelle Ammons, (Fig. 19), daughter of Milton and Minerva Moredock Ammons, was born at Rices Landing, Pennsylvania, May 23, 1889. She attended the State Normal School of California, Pennsylvania in 1909. She attended West Virginia University, receiving the bachelor of arts degree in 1917 and the master of arts degree in 1923. She attended Columbia University during the summer of 1921, University of Chicago during the summer of 1931, and received the degree of doctor of philosophy at the University of Pittsburgh in 1937.

Miss Ammons taught in the grade school at Rices Landing in 1909-1913. She taught at East Fairmont High School, West Virginia, in 1918-20, after which she started a long teaching career in botany at West Virginia University, as instructor in 1920-37, assistant professor in 1937-45, associate professor in 1945-53, and professor from 1953 until she retired in 1959.

She has held membership in the following organizations: American Association for Advancement of Science, Sigma Xi, Botanical Society of America, American Bryological Society, American Institute of Biological Sciences, W. Va. Academy of Science (treasurer, 1940-47, president in 1949), Southern Appalachian Botanical Club (treasurer from the time it was founded in 1936 until 1958), Phi Epsilon Phi, Woman's Christian

Temperance Union, Morgantown Woman's Club, Presbyterian Church, Christian Endeavor, and Y.W.C.A.

While at the University she built up a large bryophyte collection, and organized the bryophyte herbarium into a usable and workable one. All the unmounted University collections of bryophytes, including her own, were merged and arranged alphabetically according to genera. Her book on the "Liverworts of West Virginia" has been widely accepted as authoritative.

A list of most of her publications pertaining to West Virginia plant life are as follows: Spring foray of 1940. *Castanea* 5:107-109. 1940; The shrubs of West Virginia. *W. Va. Univ. Bull. Ser.* 50, 12-4. 127 pp.; (with Earl L. Core) The hollies of West Virginia. *Castanea* 10:57-60. 1945; (with Earl L. Core) The dogwoods of West Virginia. *Castanea* 10:88-90. 1945; (with Earl L. Core) Huckleberries, blueberries and cranberries of West Virginia. *Castanea* 10:103-109. 1945; Bryophytes of McKinneys Cave. *Bryologist* 36:16-19. 1933; Preliminary list of West Virginia mosses. *Bryologist* 37:65-74. 1934; A manual of the liverworts of West Virginia. *Univ. of Pitt. Bull.* 34:1-7. 1937; List of West Virginia liverworts. *Bryologist* 41:63-68. 1938; A manual of the liverworts of West Virginia. *Am. Midl. Nat.* 23:3-164. 1940; Bryophytes of the Appalachian shale barrens. *Castanea* 8:128-131; Date seed germination. *Proc. W. Va. Acad. Sci.* 1:23-25. 1926; Woody plants of West Virginia in winter condition (with Earl L. Core). Edwards Bros., Inc. 124 pp. illus. 1946; and Woody plants in winter (with Earl L. Core). The Boxwood Press, Pittsburgh, Pa. 218 pp. illus. 1958.

Robert Clifton Spangler (Fig. 22) was born near Peterstown, West Virginia, August 11, 1884. After attending a local one-room elementary school he taught school in 1904-05. He received his high school training at Marshall State Normal School, graduating in 1908. After teaching in high school in 1909-11, he entered West Virginia University, receiving the bachelor of arts degree in 1914 and the master of arts degree in 1916. He received the doctor of philosophy degree in botany at the University of Chicago in 1925. He served on the botany staff of West Virginia University, as instructor in 1914-1920, assistant professor in 1920-23, associate professor from 1923 to 1926 and professor from 1926 until his retirement in 1955.

He married Bess Farley on December 28, 1910, and to this marriage was born two sons, Robert and John, and three daughters, Helen, Phyllis and Eleanor. Two of these children, John and Helen, have the doctor of philosophy degree and were made members of Phi Beta Kappa in their junior year at West Virginia University.

Dr. Spangler is a member of the West Virginia Academy of Science, Southern Appalachian Botanical Club, and the Botanical Society of America.

He studied under Dr. Sheldon and did his first collecting under his supervision in 1911-1912. He was allowed one hour credit for each fifty plants collected and properly identified. This resulted in the collection of 200 specimens. These specimens are now in the University Herbarium and are among the first contributions to the present Herbarium.

He has written the following: *Acer carolinianum* Walt. in West Virginia. *Castanea* 4:63. 1939, and The female gametophyte of *Trillium sessile, Bot. Gaz.* 69:217-221. 1925. Although not pertaining to botany, but of interest to his former students, is a paper entitled "Control of Sex in Animals," which he read at the meeting of the West Virginia Academy of Science in 1944 (published in 1952).

Dr. Spangler received wide publicity for his controversy on evolution with the "silver-tongued orator," William Jennings Bryan, in 1922. As related to the author by Dr. Spangler, the events were as follows: A new preacher at the Christian Church of Morgantown, by the name of O. W. Baylor, criticized Dr. A. M. Reese for teaching evolution in his zoology classes at West Virginia University. Mr. Baylor arranged to have a debate on the subject at the Presbyterian Church in Morgantown on March 1. Dr. Reese spoke on the subject, "Why I should believe in Evolution," and another University professor, Dr. C. W. Waggoner, head of the physics department, spoke on "Why I should not believe in Evolution." After a series of events, this was followed, on May 11, with a lecture by William Jennings Bryan, who addressed an overflow audience in Commencement Hall (now Reynold's Hall) on the subject "The Bible and its Enemies." He stated that he had been informed that some of the teachers at the University contradicted the Bible by teaching evolution. He then stated that he would give any one $100 to cite one instance in the Bible to prove that evolution was in harmony with its teachings. He also stated that the account of creation must be taken literally. Dr. Spangler wrote Mr. Baylor, claiming $100 by answering Mr. Bryan's challenge, taking the story of creation literally. He stated that according to the account of the flood in the Bible, that it rained for 40 days and 40 nights and water covered the earth for 180 days. There was no statement of plants being taken into the Ark with the animals, and it was a known fact that land plants could not survive that long in water. Since there was no mention of special creation after the flood, the only way that plants could appear after the flood would have to be by evolution. The water plants could survive and evolve into land plants. Five weeks later Mr. Bryan sent a check for $100 to Mr. Baylor to be delivered to Dr. Spangler, with a note that Spangler had been guilty of "cowardly evasion." Dr. Spangler called on Bryan to retract his accusation. Later Mr. Bryan wrote to Dr. Spangler, retracting the accusation and asking him for an account of his ancestry. He replied by stating that he had started from a single cell, and gave an account of evolution. The letter was publicized by the Associated Press, and numerous letters and telegrams from all over the United States and four other countries were sent to Dr. Spangler, most of them defending him.

REFERENCES

CATTELL, J. MCKEEN. *American Men of Science* (1st ed.) New York: The Science Press. 1906. (2nd ed.), 1910.

CATTELL, J. MCKEEN AND DEAN R. BRIMHALL. *American Men of Science* (3rd ed.) New York: The Science Press, 1921.

CATTELL, J. MCKEEN AND JAQUES CATTELL. *American Men of Science* (4th ed.) New York: The Science Press, 1927 (5th ed.), 1933. (6th ed.), 1938.

CATTELL, JAQUES. *American Men of Science* (7th ed.) Lancaster: The Science Press, 1944. (8th ed.), 1949.

CATTELL, JAQUES. *American Men of Science* (9th ed.) Lancaster: The Science Press. New York: R. R. Bowker Co., 1955.

CATTELL, JAQUES. *American Men of Science* (10th ed.) Arizona State University, Tempe, Arizona: Cattell Press, Inc., 1960.

West Virginia University Catalog, West Virginia University Bulletin, 1867-68 to 1961-62.

CHAPTER XI

Marshall University

Marshall College (University) was founded as Marshall Academy in 1837 by a group of citizens of Cabell County. The meeting was held at the home of John Laidley, who chose the name "Marshall" in honor of his close friend, John Marshall, Chief Justice of the Supreme Court, who had died two years earlier. In 1858 the name was changed to Marshall College. Near the beginning of the Civil War the institution was sold for debt. In 1867, four years after the formation of the new state of West Virginia, the legislature passed an act creating a normal school " . . . to be called West Virginia State Normal School . . . to be established at Marshall College in the County of Cabell."

College preparatory as well as teacher training work was offered. By 1886 there was a full "academical" course of two years. Through the later years of the nineteenth century, and the first two decades of the twentieth, the college offered two years of liberal arts work and two years of teacher training, in addition to the secondary work.

In 1920 the West Virginia State Board of Education approved the granting of a bachelor's degree in education. Four degrees were conferred in June, 1921 by the Teachers College. The College of Arts and Sciences was established in 1923, and awarded the first degrees in 1925. Six departments offered graduate work in 1938, and the Graduate School was authorized in May, 1948. Marshall College was elevated to the status of Marshall University in 1961.

The School Catalogue in 1886-87 listed "Natural History" as a course of instruction in the normal training course in the senior year with Hooker's or Morse's texts being used, but it was not offered in the academic course. In 1890-91 botany was taught to seniors in the normal training course, with Wood's text being used. In 1897-98 the academic department offered botany during the first term of the junior year, with Wood's or Gray's "School and Field Book of Botany" as the text. The catalogue stated under the heading of Natural Science, "The hills of Southwestern West Virginia, Southeastern Ohio, and Northeastern Kentucky furnish rare opportunities for the study of field botany." The 1909-10 catalogue stated that a herbarium was being added to the equipment. In 1918-19 two botany courses and one bacteriology course were offered in the biology department. In 1926-27 the courses offered included Plant Nutrition, Systematic Botany, Tri-State Flora, and some botany in a nature study course.

In 1927-28 Dr. Frank Albert Gilbert joined the staff, and the botany department was organized. Within a few years Marshall College became much better known, botanically speaking. Dr. Gilbert and later members of his staff have developed a progressive botany department. The growth of the department can be illustrated by the course offerings at about ten year intervals.

In 1927-28 the courses offered were as follows: Botany 103. General Botany; Botany 104. An Introduction to Systematic Botany; Botany 202. General Bacteriology; Botany 206. Nature Study; Botany 303. Mycology and Plant Pathology; Botany 304. Plant Taxonomy.

The courses offered in 1937-38 were as follows: Botany 203. General Botany; Botany 204. Cryptogamic Botany; Botany 302. General Bacteriology; Botany 305. Economic Botany; Botany 402. Advanced Bacteriology Laboratory; Botany 403. Mycology and Plant Pathology; Botany 404. Plant Taxonomy.

By 1948-49, with the establishment of the Graduate School, the courses offered were as follows: Botany 203. General Botany; Botany 209. General Botany; Botany 301. Dendrology; Botany 302. General Bacteriology; Botany 304. Plant Physiology; Botany 305. Economic Botany; Botany 402. Advanced Bacteriology Laboratory; Botany 403. Plant Pathology; Botany 404. Plant Taxonomy.

Graduate Courses (listed under Biological Sciences): Botany 504. Problems in Plant Physiology; Botany 505. Advanced Economic Botany; Botany 511. Bacteriology; Botany 515. Advanced Plant Morphology; Botany 550, 551, 552. Special Problems; Botany 580, 581. Thesis or Problem Report.

In 1962 the botany department offered the following courses: Botany 203. General Botany; Botany 301. Trees and Shrubs; Botany 302. General Bacteriology; Botany 304. Plant Physiology; Botany 305. Economic Botany; Botany 315. Plant Morphology; Botany 316. Local Plants; Botany 403. Plant Pathology; Botany 410. Special Topics.

In the Graduate School the following courses were offered under Biological Sciences: 604. Plant Physiology; 605. Advanced Economic Botany; 611. Bacteriology; 615. Advanced Plant Morphology; 616. Plant Taxonomy; 630. Ecology; 650, 651, 652. Special Topics; 660, 661, 662. Seminar; 680, 681. Thesis or Problem Report.

No attempt has been made to give a complete account of the development of botany at Marshall College. Biographical sketches of the following botanists certainly include some of the most important developments.

Frank Albert Gilbert, (Fig. 21), son of Frank A. and Nellie Welch Gilbert, was born in Exeter, New Hampshire, March 22, 1900. He was married to Eleanor Marshall, August 13, 1929. To this marriage were born three sons, Carter Rowell, Robert Frank, and William Marshall. He received the bachelor of Science degree at the University of Massachusetts in 1922, and from Harvard University he received the master of arts degree in 1925 and the doctor of philosophy degree in 1927.

Before joining the botany staff at Marshall College, he served as plant pathologist with the United States Department of Agriculture in 1922-23. Also, while at Harvard, he was a member of the Harvard University Botanical Expedition to Newfoundland and Labrador in 1925. At Marshall he served as assistant professor of botany in 1927-28, associate professor in 1928-29, and professor in 1929-42. While at Marshall he served as head of the botany department.

After leaving Marshall in 1942, he served as lieutenant colonel in the United States Army Reserves in the Chemical Corps until 1945. From 1945 to 1959 he was biological consultant at the Battelle Memorial Institute, Columbus, Ohio. Since 1959 he has served as professor of botany at Union College, Barbourville, Kentucky.

While at Marshall in 1927-42, he made a careful study of the flora of the southwestern counties, and built up the Marshall College Herbarium to approximately 15,000 numbers. Complete duplicates of his collections were donated to the West Virginia University Herbarium. Many of the numbers were collected in Cabell County and were distributed in centuries to at least twenty-five herbaria in the country, including Gray Herbarium, New York Botanical Garden Herbarium, United States National Herbarium, and the University of Pennsylvania Herbarium. While at Marshall he also built up a microscopic collection and lantern slide collection of about two thousand items each, and about twenty reels of motion picture film on botanical subjects.

He is a member of the Botanical Society of America, Mycological Society of America, American Association for the Advancement of Science, Horticultural Society of America, New England Botanical Club, Southern Appalachian Botanical Club (president, 1936), Sigma Xi, Gamma Alpha, Chi Beta Phi, Kiwanis, Council, Boy Scouts of America, Lambda Chi Alpha, Masons, and the Congregational Church.

His writings of interest to botanists in West Virginia are as follows: Additions to the cryptogamic flora of West Virginia. *Proc. W. Va. Acad. Sci.* 6:27-28. 1933; Additions to the slime mold flora of West Virginia. *Proc. W. Va. Acad. Sci.* 8:38-39. 1935; Additions to the cryptogamic flora of West Virginia (No. 2) *Proc. W. Va. Acad. Sci.* 9:37-38. 1936; Notes on some plants from southern West Virginia. *Jour. So. Appalach. Bot. Club* (now *Castanea*) 1:22-23. 1936; Dimerism in the genera *Trillium* and *Iris*. *Castanea* 1:89-91. 1936; Notes on plants of southern West Virginia II. *Castanea* 3:68-70. 1938; Notes on plants from southern West Virginia III. *Castanea* 3:81-84. 1938; New stations for *Asplenium ebenoides*. *Castanea* 4:58-60. 1939; Notes on plants from southern West Virginia IV. *Castanea* 6:12-14. 1941; Notes on plants from southern West Virginia V. *Castanea* 7:11-12. 1942; and (with N. Bayard Green and Edward Seeber) The biology of McCullough's Pond. *Proc. W. Va. Acad. Sci.* 15:107-110. 1942.

Hollie Clayton Darlington (Fig. 23) was born at Wriston, West Virginia, June 28, 1890, a son of James W. and Hattie Elizabeth Darlington. He attended West Virginia University, receiving the bachelor of arts degree in 1923 and the master of arts degree in 1927. He received the doctor of philosophy degree in botany at the University of Chicago in 1947.

After teaching in elementary schools for five years and high school for seven years he became a member of the staff of the science department of Teachers College, at Marshall College, serving as instructor in 1930-32, assistant professor in 1932-35, associate professor in 1935-42, and professor in 1942-57.

He is a member of the West Virginia Academy of Science, Unitarian Church, and the Universalist Society.

Dr. Darlington has contributed notably to the knowledge of the flora of southern West Virginia. In connection with his doctoral program at the University of Chicago, he made a thorough study of Cranberry Glades, in Pocahontas County, for his dissertation. He has written "Vegetation and substrate in Cranberry Glades, West Virginia." *Bot. Gaz.* 104: 371-393. 1943. For the past twenty years he has been taking classes into the Glades from Marshall University and West Virginia Institute of Technology, and since 1962 he is conducting monthly tours through the Glades for anyone who wishes to make the trip. These tours are sponsored by Jim Comstock, publisher of the *West Virginia Hillbilly* at Richwood, West Virginia.

Edward Lewis Plymale was born near Kenova, West Virginia, September 20, 1914, son of William Edward and Leah (Malcolm) Plymale. He received the bachelor of arts degree from Marshall College in 1935, the master of science degree from University of Kentucky in 1939, the doctor of philosophy degree from Iowa State University in 1942, and a Certificate in Meteorology from the University of Chicago in 1943.

After serving as meteorologist in the United States Navy in 1943-46, Dr. Plymale has served in the Botany Department of Marshall University as assistant professor in 1946-50, associate professor in 1950-54, and as professor since 1954 and the chairman of the department since 1946.

He is a member of the Botanical Society of America, American Association for the Advancement of Science, and the American Association of University Professors.

His collections of plants, largely from southern West Virginia, are in the herbaria of Marshall University and West Virginia University. His publications deal mainly with taxonomy of vascular plants of southern West Virginia. (See his "*Trichomanes Boschianum* in West Virginia." *Am. Fern Jour.* 28:122-123. 1938; "New plants for West Virginia." *Castanea* 4:61-62. 1939; and "Plants of Wayne County, West Virginia." *Castanea* 5:75-87. 1940.)

Donald David Cox was born at Maben, West Virginia, August 2, 1926. He attended Marshall College, receiving the bachelor of arts degree in 1949 and the master of arts degree in 1950. He received the degree of doctor of philosophy in plant science at Syracuse University in 1958.

After serving in the United States Navy in 1944-46, and as a public school teacher in 1949-50, he has served in the Science Department of Teachers College at Marshall University as instructor in 1950-53, assistant professor in 1954-59, associate professor since 1959, and as department chairman since 1957.

During the summers of 1958 and 1959 Dr. Cox studied bogs in the state of New York in order to determine the nature of post-glacial forests by the use of pollen analysis. More recently he has studied the bogs of West Virginia.

Howard Leonard Mills was born in Huntington, West Virginia, May 8, 1920. After receiving the degree of bachelor of science in 1944 and the degree of master of science in 1949 at Marshall College, he served as instructor in the botany department at Iowa State University in 1949-51, receiving the doctor of philosophy degree from this institution in 1951.

Dr. Mills has served in the Botany Department of Marshall University in the fields of bacteriology, plant physiology and morphology, as assistant professor in 1951-55, associate professor in 1955-61, and professor since 1961. He was a fellow of the National Science Foundation—Atomic Energy Commission in the summer of 1959, and was Research Associate at Highlands University, Las Vegas, New Mexico in 1959-60. He served in the United States Navy Reserve as lieutenant in 1943-46.

He is a member of the Botanical Society of America, and the Society of Plant Physiologists.

His research has dealt largely with his field of specialization, including physiology of growth and floral initiation; anthocyanin production and localization; algal nutrition; bactericides; radiobotany; and fission product uptake by plant roots.

James Pittard Gillespie was born November 21, 1931, at Peiping, China, the son of American Southern Baptist missionaries. He received the bachelor of science degree in biology at Wake Forest College in 1953, and the master of science degree in botany at the University of Tennessee in 1955. He has taken additional graduate work at the University of Florida, the University of Michigan, and Iowa State University. He has specialized in taxonomy and cytology of phanerogams.

In 1961 Mr. Gillespie joined the science staff at Marshall University. His publications are as follows: The genus Heuchera in Tennessee. *Journ. Tenn. Acad. Sci.* 31(3):232-241. 1956; The Hypericaceae of Tennessee. *Castanea* 24:24-32. 1959; A theory of relationships in the *Lycopodium inundatum* complex. *Amer. Fern Journ.* 52(1):19-26. 1962; Let's look at Mikes. S-9 2(3):9-12, 62, 63. 1963. (Cowan Pub. Corp.) March, 1963; (With Katherine Lim Chen) The chromosome crusher: An innovation for sore thumbs. *Castanea* 27:163-164.

1962; (With Richard W. Pohl) Distributional and cytological notes on *Salsola collina*. *Rhodora* 61(730):265-267. 1959.

REFERENCES

CATTELL, JAQUES. "American Men of Science" (10th ed.) Arizona State University, Tempe, Arizona: Cattell Press, Inc., 1960.

COMSTOCK, JIM. "Cranberry Glades 1962 Tours," *The West Virginia Hillbilly*, (June, 1962), 6.

CORE, EARL L., WILLIAM H. GILLESPIE AND BETTY J. GILLESPIE. "Bibliography of West Virginia Plant Life." New York: Scholar's Library, 1962.

Marshall College Catalog, Marshall College Bulletin, 1886-87 to 1960-62.

CHAPTER XII

West Virginia Colleges

Many of our state-supported colleges as well as the other colleges have evolved from the old "Academies," which were really high schools. As early as 1813 a few of the "Academies" were offering some training in natural science. For example, Shepherdstown Academy offered instruction in Greek, Latin, Euclid, surveying, rhetoric, use of globes, history, grammar, natural and moral science, composition, and elocution. In the same year Charles Town Academy also offered training in natural science.

Many of the pre-Civil War academies failed to reopen after the Reconstruction period, while some became either normal schools or colleges. New state leaders insisted that normal schools should have a place among literary and classical colleges and academies, and that classics should give place to such subjects as arithmetic, commercial law, chemistry and botany. Marshall College was designated as the "West Virginia State Normal School" in 1867 by the legislature of the new state. In April, 1869 the Fairmont Normal School was opened. West Liberty Normal opened May 2, 1870, followed by Glenville Normal School, Concord Normal School and others. Botany was offered as a part of natural science or as a separate subject. These early normal schools, which were actually high schools, gradually developed into four year State Teachers Colleges and finally State Colleges. Throughout this development botany courses have been offered, and today are fairly well developed in most of the colleges of West Virginia.

It has been very difficult to secure detailed information concerning botany and botanists in these schools. It is hoped that the biographical sketches which follow will give at least a representative account of the part West Virginia colleges have played in the history of botany in the State.

Charles Moore Roberts was born at Corry, Pennsylvania, in 1894, and died November 9, 1953. He attended Pennsylvania State College, receiving the bachelor of science degree in 1924 and the master of science degree in 1925, and did further graduate work at the University of Michigan, University of Pittsburgh, Cornell University, and West Virginia University. He served as instructor at the University of Washington in 1925, and joined the staff of Fairmont State College in 1926, remaining there until his death, at which time he held the rank of professor of botany.

Mr. Roberts made an extensive study of bryophytes in Pennsylvania and West Virginia. His collection of more than 1,000 specimens is in the West Virginia University Herbarium. (See his "*Leucobryum albidum* for West Virginia" *Bryologist* 34:22. 1931.)

George Bowyer Rossbach, (Fig. 25) son of Rev. Adolph and Malvina Hassall Rossbach, was born at Belfast, Maine, October 26, 1910. He attended Harvard University, receiving the bachelor of science degree in 1933 and the master of arts degree in biology in 1934. He received the doctor of philosophy degree at Stanford University in 1940. He did post-doctoral work on a Ford Fellowship at the University of California in 1954-55.

He served as an assistant in biology at Harvard University and Radcliffe College in 1933-35. He was junior biologist with the United States Fish and Wildlife Research, Patuxent Refuge in 1941, and in 1941-44 was connected with the Wisconsin Conservation Department. In 1944-46 he was plant quarantine inspector with the United States Department of Agriculture, Bureau of Entomology and Plant Quarantine, New York City. He served as assistant professor of biology at William and Mary College in 1946-49, and since 1949 has served as professor and head of the Department of Biology at West Virginia Wesleyan College.

He has held membership in the Society of Plant Taxonomists, California Botanical Club, Torrey Botanical Club, New England Botanical Club, Southern Appalachian Botanical Club, Wildlife Society, Forestry Association, and is advisor to the Beta Mu Chapter Beta Beta Beta at Wesleyan. He was president of West Virginia Wesleyan Chapter of American Association of University Professors, in 1960.

Dr. Rossbach has collected extensively since 1930, from various parts of the United States and Canada, and especially from Maine, West Virginia, California, and Wisconsin. His collections are in various herbaria in this country and a few elsewhere, distributed by West Virginia University, University of California, Stanford University, and by himself. Others are in the West Virginia Wesleyan College Herbarium. Through his own collecting and some exchange with West Virginia University and the University of California, he has developed a herbarium at Wesleyan of 7,000-8,000 sheets. He has also collected

Fig. 23. Hollie Clayton Darlington

Fig. 24. Israel C. White

Fig. 25. George Bowyer Rossbach

Fig. 26. Edward R. Grose

from 5,000 to 6,000 numbers, largely in triplicate, which fairly represent the vascular flora of Waldo and Knox Counties, Maine, including the islands in and off Penobscot Bay. The earlier of the Maine collections are in the herbarium of the New England Botanical Club at Gray Herbarium of Harvard University, and the remainder are now at Wesleyan. Other collections are to a great extent from western United States, and are in various herbaria. These include a few hundred specimens of *Erysimum*, the complete set of which, including several described and published types, are at Dudley Herbarium at Stanford University. His most recent collections, in June, 1960, are largely from Florida.

He has written numerous articles on taxonomy and geographical distribution, many dealing with *Erysimum*. They are not included in this history, since they do not apply directly to West Virginia. (See his "Aquatic *Utricularias*." *Rhodora* 41:113-128. 1939.) Some characters from this key were used by M. L. Fernald in his 8th edition of Gray's Manual of Botany, 1950. Key and personal identifications in part were used by Strausbaugh and Core in Flora of West Virginia, Part III, June, 1958. His principal paper on the botany of West Virginia is "Distributional and taxonomic notes on some plants collected in West Virginia and nearby states," *Castanea* 28:10-38. 1963.

Harley Donovan Bond, son of Luther A. and Josephine Romine Bond, was born in September, 1897 at Lost Creek, West Virginia. He is a graduate of Salem College with the bachelor of arts degree and of West Virginia University with the master of arts degree. He was teacher and principal in high school before joining the faculty of Salem College in 1930 as professor of biology. At Salem he has served as dean from 1935 to 1940, treasurer from 1941 to 1958, and as assistant to the president from 1958 to 1961. Since 1961 he has been Executive Secretary of the National Seventh Day Baptist Church, with offices at Plainfield, N. J.

He is a member of the West Virginia Academy of Science, National Association of Biology Teachers, American Association for the Advancement of Science, Seventh Day Baptist Church, Masons, Kiwanis Club, and various community committees.

He has made limited collections and contributions to herbaria.

Edward Rutherford Grose (Fig. 26) was born at Sago, West Virginia, January 12, 1878, a son of John A. and Nancy Jane

Allman Grose. He received his grade school education in local schools, graduated from West Virginia Conference Seminary, Buckhannon, West Virginia, in 1904, attended West Virginia University, receiving the bachelor of arts degree in 1909 and the master of arts degree in 1914. For five summers he attended the University of Virginia at the Mountain Lake Biological Station, in Giles County, Virginia.

Mr. Grose taught six terms in rural elementary schools; was principal of Littleton graded school in 1904-05; taught in New Martinsville High School in 1907-08; and was assistant district superintendent of Clay District, Harrison County in 1909-11. After teaching two spring terms at Glenville State College in 1911-12, he became a permanent member of the staff in the fall of 1912, teaching biology and mathematics. He retired in 1943.

Mr. Grose was a member of the West Virginia Academy of Science, National Geographic Society, West Virginia Biological Survey, Brooks Bird Club, Southern Appalachian Botanical Club, American Fern Society, Baptist Church, West Virginia University Emeritus Club, West Virginia Alumni Association, Farm Bureau, and West Virginia Education Association.

He has made a careful study of the flora of Gilmer and Upshur Counties. His interesting collections of mosses, ferns, lichens, and seed plants are in the University herbarium.

Mr. Grose died April 7, 1964, survived by his wife, Lulu Floyd Grose, a daughter, Mrs. Walter G. House, and two sons, Edward C. and William S.

William Douglas Creasy was born at Calvin, West Virginia, June 16, 1916. He received the bachelor of science degree at West Virginia Institute of Technology, the master of science degree at West Virginia University, and the doctor of philosophy degree from Iowa State University. He taught at Marshall College one year and three years at New Mexico Highlands University in Las Vegas, New Mexico, before joining the staff of Fairmont State College in 1954.

He has contributed about 150 specimens from Nicholas County to the West Virginia University Herbarium. (See his, "Taxonomy of *Scrophularia marilandica* L. and *S. lanceolata* Pursh." *Castanea* 18:65-68. 1953. Also "Secondary Succession and Growth of Yellow Poplar on the Green Mountain, Nicholas County, West Virginia." *Castanea* 19:81-87. 1954.)

Juanita Simons McCoy was born at Abbott, West Virginia, May 20, 1913. She graduated from Buckhannon-Upshur High

School, attended West Virginia Wesleyan College in 1930-32 and West Virginia University in 1954-58, receiving her bachelor's degree and master's degree. She has served on the biology staff at Salem College as instructor in 1955-58, and as assistant professor since 1958.

Mrs. McCoy is a member of the Southern Appalachian Botanical Club, American Fern Society, West Virginia Academy of Science, and Phi Epsilon Phi.

She has made important contributions to the West Virginia University Herbarium and the Salem College Herbarium, and has a personal herbarium of about 500 numbers. At the present time she and her husband, Paul McCoy, are building up a kodachrome slide collection of plants in West Virginia, including fungi, mosses, clubmosses, ferns, and flowering plants. For a number of years she has been working on a paper dealing with the distribution of the *Dryopteris spinulosa* complex in Northeastern United States, a projection of her master's thesis. She has annotated *Dryopteris* for several herbaria, including Gray Herbarium, University of Pennsylvania Herbarium, Penn State Herbarium, Smithsonian Herbarium, West Virginia University Herbarium, and the New York Botanical Garden Herbarium. For a number of years she has been working on a checklist and description of plants found in Harrison and Doddridge counties.

Ellis Meade McNeill, (Fig. 27), son of A. W. and Etta McNeill, was born at Buckeye, West Virginia, December 2, 1901. After completing elementary school he attended Edray District High School (Marlinton High School), and received his high school diploma in 1922. He was married to Bula McManaway, July 27, 1925. He received the bachelor of arts degree from Concord College in 1928 and the master of science degree from West Virginia University in 1930. He attended West Virginia University during the summer term of 1931, University of Virginia at Mountain Lake, Virginia, in the summer of 1935, and Duke University, various terms, receiving the doctor of philosophy degree in 1946.

After teaching a year at the Oakvale School (1927), he started his long career in biology at Concord College as an instructor in 1928, assistant professor and later associate professor from 1929-1939, professor in 1939, and head of the Department of Biology in 1943, a position which he now holds. He was a graduate assistant at Duke University during the first semester of 1936-1937, and directed the summer field botanical studies at West Virginia University 1948-1950.

Dr. McNeill is a member of the following scientific organizations: Phi Epsilon Phi, Phi Sigma, Chi Beta Phi, American Association for the Advancement of Science (Fellow), Botanical Society of America, Southern Appalachian Botanical Club, American Society of Plant Taxonomists, and the West Virginia Academy of Science. He served as Vice-President of the West Virginia Academy of Science in 1942-1943, and President in 1944-1945 and 1945-1946.

Dr. McNeill has been very active in civic, fraternal, and other community activities. He is a Royal Arch Mason, past president of the Princeton-Athens Kiwanis Club, past Kiwanis Governor for the Fourth Division, and is an Elder in the Princeton Presbyterian Church.

The publications of Dr. McNeill deal largely with his specialty, the algae, and include the following: A study of the algal flora of Shawnee Lake. *Proc. W. Va. Acad. Sci.* 10:64-69. 1937; Plant records from Mercer County, West Virginia. *Castanea* 3:36-39. 1938; A contribution to the knowledge of West Virginia algae. *Castanea* 13:1-60. 1948; and Algae of West Virginia, a chapter in "Plant Life of West Virginia" by Dr. Core. The publication "A contribution to the knowledge of West Virginia algae" was taken from his doctor's dissertation (1946). Of the 321 species, varieties and forms included in the publication 219 were reported for the first time for West Virginia; 101 had been reported previously by Fling (1920), and 1 by Wolle (1887). Unusual plants include a new genus and species, *Trichospira bula* (Myxophyceae), a new species, *Stipitococcus infundibuliformis* (Heterokontae) and *Bulbochaete mirabilis* forma *immersa* (Wittrock) Hirn. (Oedogoniaceae), a new record for North America. Included in the publication are keys to the classes, genera and species. All collections made by the writer in this survey, preserved both in liquid and on herbarium cards, are deposited at Concord College. Samples of some of the collections are deposited in the Chicago Natural History Museum.

Dr. McNeill's interest in plants was exhibited at a very early age. His mother, who was also interested in plants, encouraged him to develop this interest. While in elementary school he collected plants, pressed them in perhaps a Sears, Roebuck catalog, and dried them behind the kitchen stove. His mother helped him with the identification, using local common names.

In high school his biology teacher, Emma Myers, recognized his unusual interest and talent, helped him, and encouraged him to further his interest by going to college. While at Concord College he studied biology under Professor Frank Cutright, and was influenced to go ahead in this field. While working on a master of science degree at West Virginia University in 1929-1930 he received the real impetus to go ahead, due largely to the influence of Dr. P. D. Strausbaugh. As a member of the West Virginia University Botanical Expedition he was closely associated with Dr. Strausbaugh, and started a friendship that has been a guiding inspiration to him throughout his life.

As chairman of the Biology Department at Concord College, Dr. McNeill has had little time for extensive research and writing. He has had a full schedule, has taught a varied number of biology courses, and has taken time to deal with the many problems of his students. He exemplifies the motto of Concord College: "The friendly college on the campus beautiful." His students affectionately call him "Dr. Mac" and feel free to call on him for guidance when they have had scholastic difficulties or perhaps a spat with a boy friend or girl friend.

Dr. McNeill has had a tremendous influence on the thousands of young men and women who have studied under him. In more than a dozen counties surrounding Concord College many teachers, lawyers, doctors, and leaders in other walks of life have been inspired by his influence. Many of these individuals attended Concord College, and recall with pride that they studied biology under Dr. McNeill.

In addition to the numerous public school teachers who have studied under Dr. McNeill, several others have done graduate work in botany at West Virginia University and other universities. Prominent among these individuals is Mrs. **Dana (Stike) Evans,** who received a master of science degree in botany from West Virginia University in 1941 under the direction of Dr. P. D. Strausbaugh. She taught biology at Bluefield, McComas, and Mullens for a number of years, and in 1958 she became a member of the biology staff at Concord College. Aside from her teaching duties she has been very helpful to Dr. McNeill in preparing herbarium specimens. At the present time they have several thousand sheets of herbarium specimens at the College. She is a member of the Southern Appalachian Botanical Club, and the West Virginia Academy of Science.

Also prominent among his former students who have gone

on with graduate work in biology are the following: **John Magann,** principal of the Glenwood School, Bluefield, West Virginia, who received a master of science degree in biology at West Virginia University; **William Fox,** master of science degree from West Virginia University and doctor of philosophy degree from the University of Iowa; **Percy Lilly,** master of science degree from West Virginia University and doctor of philosophy degree from Pennsylvania State University; **James Harvey Craft** (born January 21, 1914), master of science degree from West Virginia University and doctor of philosophy degree from the University of Iowa, chairman division of science and mathematics, Adams State College, Alamosa, Colo.; **Florence Thomas,** master of science degree from West Virginia University and doctor of philosophy degree from Cornell University; and **Charles Yearout,** who received his master of science degree from West Virginia University, and operates a plant nursery at Princeton, West Virginia.

Dr. McNeill has studied the flora of southern West Virginia very thoroughly, and has done much collecting. He has been one of the leading contributors to the West Virginia University Herbarium. The four volumes of "Flora of West Virginia" by Dr. P. D. Strausbaugh and Dr. Earl L. Core, refer to many of his State and county records. Much of this collecting was done while he was pursuing two of his main hobbies, fishing and gardening. His wild flower garden contains not only many of the common wild flowers but also many of the less common or unusual plants, including *Cypripedium reginae.*

On weekends, and whenever possible, he may be seen along a trout stream or bass fishing along Greenbrier River. He often returns with an empty creel, but a full vasculum. On one occasion he was seen near Alderson wading barefooted across Greenbrier River to a small island in quest of a white bluebell. Throughout his career at Concord College he has quite frequently made trips to Buckeye to visit his parents, and on many of these trips he stops at the "Droop Mountain Glade, or Cranberry Glades," where he had spent many happy moments during his childhood.

The writer, while interviewing Dr. McNeill, attempted to delve into his metaphysical and philosophical thinking. He was quick to give assurance that he had no atheistic tendencies, and felt that there is no real conflict between science and religion. He reflected on the beauty of nature and the orderly operation of the universe and of life. He mentioned the brilliant hues of autumn leaves and the appearance of the beautiful array of spring flowers, etc. He felt he could perhaps be called a pantheist, but never an atheist.

Wilbur John Sumpstine was born in Somerset, Pennsylvania, June 27, 1901, and died September 30, 1945. He received his bachelor of science degree from Bethany College in 1925, his master's degree from the University of Chicago, and had nearly completed a doctor of philosophy degree from the University of Pittsburgh. He taught biology at Bethany College for a number of years, and at the time of his death had the rank of professor of biology.

He was a member of the West Virginia Academy of Science, Southern Appalachian Botanical Club, American Association for the Advancement of Science, and the Association of American Biology Teachers.

He made a careful study of the flora in his vicinity, and was working on a survey of flora of the western panhandle of West Virginia, at the time of his death. (See his "Origin and development of the tissues in the rhizomes of *Onoclea sensibilis*." *Proc. W. Va. Acad. Sci.* 5:37-42 1931; "Additions to the range of *Pinus strobus* in West Virginia." *Proc. W. Va. Acad. Sci.* 11:44. 1938.) His large collection of plants is in the Herbarium of West Virginia University.

Adolph Putman Hamblin was born at Galesburg, Illinois, January 11, 1896. He graduated from Galesburg High School in 1915. He received his bachelor of science degree at Knox College (Galesburg, Illinois) in 1920 and his master of science degree at Ohio State University in 1946.

Mr. Hamblin organized the Department of Biology at West Virginia State College in 1920, serving as professor and chairman of the department since that time.

He is a member of Beta Kappa Chi, national honorary scientific society, and sponsor of the West Virginia State College Chapter; associate member of Sigma Xi, Ohio State University Chapter; and the West Virginia Academy of Science. He also is a member of the Colonel Young Post of the American Legion at Charleston, West Virginia, and Omega Psi Phi fraternity.

He has made a rather large collection of wet and dry mounted study materials and museum mounts of plants indigenous to West Virginia and particularly of the Charleston and Kanawha Valley area. This valuable collection of algae, fungi, lichens, bryophytes, pteridophytes, angiosperms and gymnosperms is displayed at West Virginia State College.

His master's thesis was entitled, "An illustrated key to the more important vascular plant families of West Virginia." He also has prepared in mimeograph form, a number of keys for the identification of plants, including algae, tree leaves, fungi, and others.

Max Ward was born at Grantsville, West Virginia, May 14, 1914. He received the bachelor of arts degree from Glenville State College in 1940. He attended Harvard University, receiving the master of arts degree in 1947 and the doctor of philosophy degree in 1950. Before joining the staff at Glenville State College he taught in grade schools and high schools for five and one-half years. He has been a member of the staff at Glenville for twelve years, and chairman of the science division since 1958.

Dr. Ward is a member of the West Virginia Academy of Science, American Association for the Advancement of Science, Botanical Society of America, American Bryological Society, and New England Botanical Club.

His publications are as follows:

Fertilization in *Phlebodium aureum* J. Sm. *Phytomorphology* 4:1-17. 1954.

The development of the embryo of *Phlebodium aureum* J. Sm. *Phytomorphology* 4:18-26. 1954.

(With R. H. Wetmore) Experimental control of development in the embryo of the fern *Phlebodium aureum* J. Sm. *Am. Jour. Bot.* 41:428-434. 1954.

Callus tissues from the mosses *Polytrichum* and *Atrichum*. *Science* 132:1401-1402. 1960.

Some techniques in the culture of mosses. *Bryologist* 63:213-217. 1960.

Vegetative propagation from intact leaves of *Polytrichum*. *Phytomorphology* 10:325-329. 1960.

Adventitious sporophytes of gametophytic origin in *Phlebodium aureum*. *Jour. Linnaean Society London.* 1962.

Verona Mapel 1854-1933. *Castanea* 20:25-27. 1955.

Joseph Francis Glencoe, Jr. was born September 7, 1936, at Davis, West Virginia. He graduated from Davis High School in 1954. He attended Potomac State College in 1956-1957, and then attended West Virginia University, receiving the bachelor of arts degree in biology in 1959 and the master of science degree in botany in 1962.

Mr. Glencoe served on the biology staff of Potomac State

College in 1961-62, and in 1962 joined the staff of Morris Harvey College.

Violet S. Phillips, a daughter of Tony and Stella Siemioczko, was born August 2, 1918, at Kingston, West Virginia. She received the bachelor of science degree from West Virginia Institute of Technology in 1942 and the master of science degree from West Virginia University in 1946, and has also taken post-graduate courses at the University during the summer terms.

Mrs. Phillips taught at East Bank High School for six years before joining the biology staff at West Virginia Institute of Technology in 1948. Presently she is assistant professor in the biology department and also teaches the courses in botany.

She is a member of the American Association for the Advancement of Science and the West Virginia Academy of Science.

Verona Mapel (Fig. 31) was born December 28, 1854, in Spragg, Greene County, Pennsylvania. She graduated from Fairmont Normal School in 1879, and also attended Radcliffe College. She taught at Glenville Normal School from 1882 to 1894, the last two years serving as acting principal of the school. She spent the next term teaching at West Liberty Normal School.

She married Linn Brannon, a lawyer and jurist of Glenville, in 1895, and lived there for ten years. They had one child, Linn Mapel Brannon. The family moved to Weston, West Virginia, in 1905, and Mrs. Brannon died there on October 16, 1933.

At Glenville Miss Mapel taught literature, botany, and mathematics. Students were impressed by her charm, brilliance, dynamic personality, and helpfulness in their identification and making of herbarium collections.

While Miss Mapel was teacher of botany at Glenville and afterwards, she collected and identified native plants in the immediate area, as well as in Ohio and New England. Millspaugh, in his "Living Flora of West Virginia" credits her with having collected about 355 species from 1881 to 1901, not including "common weeds nor the grasses and sedges." Her personal herbarium of some size, has apparently been lost. In addition to her collecting, she studied aspects of botanical morphology, and on occasion lectured on the subject to the students in Weston High School.

"Her flower garden at Weston grew to notable proportions. A sister-in-law, Mrs. Howard Brannon of Glenville, describes Miss Mapel as possessing the proverbial and highly practical 'green thumb'. She grew numerous wild flowers, and later developed an extended interest in exotic trees and shrubs. Her son notes that she grew a ginkgo tree from seed. This 50 year old tree, now about 65 feet in height, stands at 236 Center Street in Weston. It is the only significant remnant of a garden that was once graced by two or three original hybrid roses developed by Miss Mapel from her extensive rose collection. In spare moments, her son recalls, she prepared and contributed a number of short articles on botany and gardening to various journals."[1]

Mrs. Brannon was instrumental in organizing two local chapters of the Daughters of the American Revolution, and also served as its state regent. She took an active part in the Weston Woman's Club.

As a lasting tribute by Glenville State College to a former teacher and principal, Verona Mapel Hall was dedicated to her in 1926.

Bernal Robinson Weimer was born at Port Royal, Pennsylvania, December 4, 1894. He attended West Virginia University, receiving the bachelor of arts degree in 1916 and the master of science degree in 1918. He received the doctor of philosophy degree in zoology at the University of Chicago in 1927.

After serving as a school superintendent in Pennsylvania in 1919-21 he joined the staff of Bethany College, serving as professor of biology since 1921, dean of the faculty from 1935 until 1962, and acting president in 1953.

Although Dr. Weimer is primarily a zoologist and biologist he teaches some botany. He is well known for his general biology college textbooks and laboratory manuals with P. D. Strausbaugh and Earl L. Core.

David L. Banks was born at Lynchburg, Virginia, March 8, 1925. He received the bachelor of science degree at Bluefield State College in 1948, and the master of science degree at West Virginia University in 1950. As a member of the staff of Bluefield State College for nine years, he has taught several courses in botany.

He is a member of the American Association for the Advancement of Science, West Virginia Academy of Science, New

[1]Max Ward, "Verona Mapel 1854-1933," *Castanea* 20:25-27. 1955.

York Academy of Science, Beta Kappa Chi, and Alpha Phi Alpha.

Charles R. Gilbert was born August 28, 1908. He attended the University of Kansas, receiving the bachelor of arts degree in 1931 and the master of arts degree in 1934. He has received further training at the University of Kansas during the summers of 1942, 1944, 1947, 1959 and 1960. As a member of the staff of Bluefield State College for twenty-seven years, he has taught several courses in botany.

He is a member of the American Association for the Advancement of Science, West Virginia Academy of Science, Beta Kappa Chi, and Kappa Alpha Psi.

REFERENCES

AMBLER, CHARLES H. "A History of Education in West Virginia." Huntington: Standard Printing and Publishing Company, 1951.

HUNT, GEORGE R. "Charles Moore Roberts," *Castanea* 18:131. 1953.

WARD, MAX. "Verona Mapel 1854-1933," *Castanea* 20:25-27. 1955.

WEIMER, B. R. "William John Sumpstine," *Castanea* 10:120. 1945.

CHAPTER XIII

Amateur Botanists of West Virginia

In botany as well as in ornithology and other fields of science, amateurs have made important contributions. We have already discussed the contributions of Lawrence William Nuttall, a mine operator in Fayette County, and a "Father" of botany in West Virginia. Scores of other amateur botanists could be mentioned, whose contributions range from minor ones to those which are very significant. Only a representative number of these individuals are discussed in this brief history.

Caroline Dane Bedinger (Danske Dandridge) was born in 1854 in Copenhagen. Her father, Henry Bedinger, who was United States minister to the Court of Denmark at the time, gave her the pet name of "Danske."

Mrs. Bedinger and children moved to Shepherdstown, Virginia (now West Virginia) and were joined by Mr. Bedinger on his return from Denmark in 1859. Friends greeted him with a barbecue at Harper's Ferry, but he took pneumonia on the horseback ride home and died shortly afterwards.

Danske was the youngest of three talented children, who took to literature from an early age. Danske dedicated a volume of poetry to the Hon. Alexander R. Boteler when she was but eleven years of age. Her older sister, Mary, was also a gifted poet and wrote for *Century Magazine* under the pen name of Mariah Blunt.

Danske was married to Adam Stephen Dandridge in 1877. Following her marriage she wrote and published several volumes of poetry, and also began the serious study of botany. Desirous of knowing the trees and shrubs of West Virginia, she planted a large grove surrounding her country home "Rose Brake" near Shepherdstown.

When she sold a poem to a magazine, she would spend her earnings beautifying Rose Brake. She finally had 500 different kinds of trees and shrubs surrounding her home, as well as a large number of herbaceous plants, which she knew and wrote about in various horticultural magazines in this country and in England. Her plant-loving friends in many countries sent seeds and plants for her estate. She had 60 kinds of spiraeas. She was a prodigious writer, and her articles appeared in numerous magazines. The English magazine, *The Garden*, published many of her articles under the heading, "Letters from Rose Brake." The magazine, *Forest and Stream*, published another series called "Notes from West Virginia." Other series were also published, including "My Garden from Day to Day," and "The Hammock under the Oaks." Her articles were also published by other magazines, including *Garden and Forest, Park and Cemetery,* and *Gardening.* A large note book in which she kept published articles cut from magazines, is still kept at Rose Brake.

The following partial list of articles published in *Garden and Forest* during one year illustrates the extent and nature of her writings.

1. The Shrubbery. November 25, 1891.
2. An Evergreen Shrubbery. January 13, 1892.
3. Spring in West Virginia. March 2, 1892.
4. *Phajus grandifolius* in window-garden. April 20, 1892.
5. Early May in West Virginia. May 18, 1892.
6. Mid-May in West Virginia. June 1, 1892.
7. May in West Virginia. June 8, 1892.
8. The Time of Roses. June 11, 1892.
9. Mid-June in West Virginia. May 22, 1892.
10. Late June in the Garden. July 6, 1892.
11. Some interesting plants. July 13, 1892.
12. In the Company of Trees. July 20, 1892.
13. A Bed of Hardy Annuals. July 27, 1892.
14. Hard Times in West Virginia. November 2, 1892.
15. Mid-October in West Virginia. November 9, 1892.
16. Notes from West Virginia. November 16, 1892.

"Her writings form an important portion of the botanical literature of West Virginia."[1] A reprint of one of her papers from *Garden and Forest,* March 2, 1892, "Spring in West Virginia" (*Castanea* 16:140-142. 1951) well illustrates her beautiful style of classic simplicity. The 70 journals and notebooks she left testify to a life of labor. While she was mainly interested in trees, shrubs and flowers, she wrote some historical books in later years, including "Historic Shepherdstown," "George Michael Bedinger, A Kentucky Pioneer," "American Prisoners of the Revolution," and "St. Clair's Defeat."

Mrs. Dandridge died in 1914.

[1]Earl L. Core. "Danske Dandridge." *Castanea* 16:139. 1951.

Hamilton McSparrin Gamble, son of James Carr Gamble and Mrs. Elizabeth Maria Williams Gamble, was born on October 25, 1838, in Moorefield, Virginia, where he spent most of his life. From early childhood he was a lover of nature, and spent much time along the banks of the South Branch of the Potomac and in the hills and mountains of the area.

He attended Virginia Military Institute from 1853 to 1856. In 1856 he was a student at the Norfolk Academy, and early in 1857 went to Kalamazoo, Michigan, where he began the study of medicine under his brother-in-law, Dr. Foster Pratt. While there he spent some time in a drug store learning the practical part of pharmacy. In 1858 he attended the University of Michigan, and graduated in pharmacy in 1859. He then attended the Jefferson Medical College, in Philadelphia, and graduated in 1861, just at the start of the Civil War. At once he enlisted as a private in the Confederate Army and in 1862 was appointed by Jefferson Davis as a surgeon, in which capacity he served until the end of the war.

Dr. Gamble returned to Moorefield at the close of the war, and began his career of medicine and surgery. He was widely known as a skillful surgeon. For a number of years he was French translator and a contributor of original articles to Gaillard's *Medical Journal of New York*, and for a number of years after Dr. Gaillard's death was assistant editor of the *Journal*. He became widely known by the medical profession and was ranked at the top of his profession.

In addition to his high rank in his profession, his general education was of a high order. He was a master of French, German and Latin languages, and could read Greek, Spanish, and Italian. In recognition of his ability and reputation, West Virginia University awarded him the honorary degree of doctor of philosophy on June 13, 1894.

He did considerable herbalizing in the valley of the South Branch of the Potomac River, and its watershed in Hardy, Grant, Mineral and Hampshire counties from 1889 until his death in 1917. In 1891, he donated his plant collections of 157 species to West Virginia University, and it represents one of the oldest portions of the present herbarium. It was from specimens sent to Asa Gray that the location "W. Va." was credited for some species in the 6th edition of Gray's Manual. On April 23, 1954, Gamble Garden in the West Virginia University Arboretum was named in his honor. (*Arboretum Newsletter*, Vol. 4, No. 2, March-April 1954.)

Rufus Davis Alderson (1858-1932) was born in Alderson, Virginia (now West Virginia), November 2, 1858. At the age of 15 he was already interested in botany and was identifying native plants, as shown by notes in his copy of Wood's Class-Book. He became a school teacher and later publisher of the Alderson *Statesman*. From 1887 to 1897 he was in California, during much of the time teaching in various schools in San Diego County. From 1893 to 1897 he made extensive botanical collections (several thousand numbers), including many duplicates that were exchanged or sold and are now found in several public herbaria. In 1897 he returned to West Virginia in rather frail health. Advised by his doctor to work outdoors, he took up cattle breeding and dairy farming. He died May 11, 1932.

Dr. Millspaugh's reference to R. W. Alderson[2] no doubt was R. D. Alderson. An examination of R. D. Alderson's signature shows that he made an open "D." which could easily be mistaken for a "W.".

William Earl Rumsey (1865-1938), was born at Vanetten, New York, September 9, 1865. He attended school in his home town before entering Cornell University in 1887. He studied under J. H. Comstock, and graduated in 1891 with the degree of bachelor of science in agriculture. His association with Professor Comstock, no doubt, was responsible for his choice of entomology as his favorite field of work.

In 1892 he came to Morgantown as a member of the staff of the Agricultural Experiment Station of West Virginia University. He served as assistant entomologist of the Experimental Station until 1913, state entomologist from 1913 to 1934 and from 1934 until the time of his death served as the Experiment Station photographer.

Mr. Rumsey's interest was not confined to entomology. He was also interested in botany, and served as instructor of botany during one semester of 1897-98 term, in addition to his duties as botanist and assistant entomologist, at the Agricultural Experiment Station. He maintained a keen interest in plants throughout his life, planted unusual species about his home, and added many numbers to the University Herbarium. He was interested in nature and enjoyed hiking through the woods with friends. "On one occasion, accompanied by three other hikers, Mr. Rumsey was leading the way along a narrow mountain path. Suddenly he stopped and whispered, "Listen,

[2] C. F. Millspaugh, "Botanical Field Work in the State." *W. Va. Geol. Surv.* 5(A) (Wheeling: Wheeling News Litho. Company, 1913), 11.

listen!" We listened intently for one or two minutes and then the next to him whispered, "What do you hear?" To this Mr. Rumsey replied, "Oh, the silence. Isn't it fine?" This was not intended as a joke; he was expressing sincerely what he so keenly felt."[3]

One of the West Virginia University Arboretum nature trails, "Rumsey Trail," was dedicated to his memory in 1961 (See *Arboretum Newsletter,* Vol. 11, No. 1. 1961).

Fred William Gray, (Fig. 28), son of James Milton and Mary Elizabeth Gray, was born in Anson County, North Carolina, in 1878. He received the bachelor of arts degree from Catawba College in 1905, the bachelor of divinity degree from Union Theological Seminary, Richmond, Virginia, in 1908, and the honorary degree of doctor of divinity from Davis and Elkins College in 1929. He was a minister in the Presbyterian Church, and served as pastor of various churches in West Virginia, Virginia, and St. Louis, Missouri. For a number of years he served as superintendent of Home Missions in the Greenbrier Presbytery of West Virginia, and he was the moderator of this Presbytery for two terms, and of the Synod of West Virginia for one term. From 1932 until his retirement he served as pastor of churches in Philippi and Belington. After he retired, he moved to Riverdale, Maryland, where he resided for the last 12 years of his life.

Although he was successful in his profession as a minister, he was widely known for his contributions to the botany of West Virginia, and was well and favorably known among his many botanical friends as "Parson" Gray. He was also widely known for his work with the culture of gladioli, introducing a number of popular new hybrids. He also contributed articles to various publications dealing with the growing of gladiolus, including Yearbook (Gladiolus-growing), The Illinois Glad Bulletin, "Gladiolus," Calgary, Canada, and the New Zealand Yearbook.

Rev. Gray made careful studies of the mountain region of West Virginia from 1920 onwards, resulting in new records of seed plants, but ferns, mosses, liverworts, and lichens were his chief concern. His large herbarium of nearly 24,000 specimens, was acquired by the University in 1939.

He is described by Dr. P. D. Strausbaugh, who botanized

[3]P. D. Strausbaugh, "William Earl Rumsey." *Castanea* 3:53-54. 1938.

with him and who knew him well, as "a man of boundless energy—an enthusiastic and vigorous collector of plants of all kinds, especially bryophytes, ferns and lichens. He was an unusually keen observer and few if any field botanists were able to so readily detect variations in form and appearance." He further states "But Rev. Gray was more than a mere collector of plants; he was a keen observer and a careful, meticulous student. He had a large correspondence with botanists both in the United States and in foreign countries. He discovered a considerable number of new varieties and new forms, and contributed articles to *American Archaeology, The Bryologist, American Fern Journal,* and *Torreya.*

"Rev. Gray's work as a minister was his chief concern. He considered his work with plants a hobby but the results derived from his hobby gave him a definite place among the productive botanists. His was a contagious spirit which inspired others to try 'to go and do likewise' . . . On the 9th of March, 1960, he departed, leaving with us an imperishable and pleasant memory."[4]

(See his "Scores of stations for *Gaylussacia brachycera.*" *Torreya* 22:17-18. 1922.; "Ferns of eastern West Virginia." *Am. Fern Jour.* 14:1-13. 1924; "An explanation of the occurrence of certain new Cladonias," *Bryologist* 35:18-23. 1932.)

Hannibal A. Davis (born August 1, 1899) and his wife, **Tyreeca,** have contributed notably to botany in West Virginia by their contributions to the West Virginia University Herbarium and by their publications. Dr. Davis is a native of Marshall County, West Virginia. He attended West Virginia University, receiving his bachelor's degree (1923) and master's degree (1925). He received the doctor of philosophy degree at Cornell University in 1928. He is professor of mathematics at West Virginia University, and has been a member of the staff since 1921. He and his wife spend much of their spare time making discriminating collections and studies of plants in West Virginia and other states. They have contributed thousands of specimens to the University Herbarium, including numerous first records for West Virginia. They have thoroughly studied the genus *Viola* and the genus *Rubus* in West Virginia. They have discovered several species of *Rubus* in West Virginia which are new to science. In addition to their collecting they have a flower garden, containing about 2000 species of plants.

[4]P. D. Strausbaugh, "Rev. Fred W. Gray," *Castanea* 25:132. 1960.

Liberty Hyde Bailey, of Cornell University, named in honor of them *Rubus davisiorum,* a groundberry which they discovered in 1946 near Cranesville (*Gentes Herbarum* 7:208. 1947). Species of *Rubus* named by Dr. and Mrs. Davis include *R. caponensis* (*Castanea* 18:21. 1953), *R. orbicularis* (*Castanea* 18:17. 1953), *R. canaanensis* (*Castanea* 18:23. 1953), *R. concameratus* (*Castanea* 18:24. 1953), *R. fryei* (*Castanea* 18:26. 1953), *R. leggii* (*Castanea* 18:27. 1953), *R. prestonensis* (*Castanea* 18:28. 1953), *R. densissimus* (*Castanea* 18:29. 1953), and *R. tygartensis* (*Castanea* 18:30. 1953). Several other species of *Rubus,* discovered by them in West Virginia, were named by Dr. Bailey.

A partial list of their publications is as follows:

The violets of West Virginia. *Castanea* 14:53-87. 1949.

Rubus concentrations along the West Virginia-Maryland Border. *Castanea* 16:101-104. 1951.

The genus *Rubus* in West Virginia—A preliminary report. *Proc. W. Va. Acad. Sci.* 23:37-43. 1951.

The genus *Rubus* in West Virginia. *Castanea* 18:1-31. 1953.

Dr. Davis has also written as follows:

(With Carleton R. Ball) The willows of West Virginia. *Castanea* 12:94-100. 1947.

(With Earl L. Core and Earl E. Berkley) West Virginia grasses. *W. Va. Agr. Exp. Sta. Bull.* 313:1-96. 1944.

(With Earl L. Core) Spermatophytes new to West Virginia. *Castanea* 5:20-23. 1940.

(See bibliography of Earl L. Core in Chapter VIII for a complete list of his publications with Dr. Core.)

Eugene Elihu Hutton, Jr. was born in Huttonsville, West Virginia, on February 14, 1913, and received his elementary and secondary education in the local schools. He received his bachelor's degree at Davis and Elkins College in 1934 where he majored in pre-medicine. He taught in a one-room school near Huttonsville in 1934 and taught biology in Elkins High School from 1935 to 1942. He then entered the Medical College of Virginia and received his M.D. degree in 1946. His practice has been in Elkins for the past twelve years.

He is a member of the Presbyterian Church, American Medical Association, W. Va. State Medical Association, Barbour-Randolph-Tucker County Medical Society, Elks Lodge No. 1135, Randolph County Historical Society, Elkins Rotary Club, Southern Appalachian Botanical Club, Washington, D. C., Ski

Club, and has served as a member of the Randolph County Board of Education.

Dr. Hutton has studied the native flora of Randolph County for a number of years. A new species of *Rubus* which he discovered in Randolph County was named *R. huttonii* by Liberty Hyde Bailey (*Gentes Herbarum* 7:206. 1947). He was also instrumental in rediscovering *R. roribaccus* at its original station in Randolph County. He has collected numerous plants in the Randolph County area since 1940, which he has contributed to the West Virginia University Herbarium. Among these are included some of the first records for West Virginia, including *Carex canescens* (see Castanea 6:144-145. 1941.); *Zigadeneus leimanthoides* at Cheatbridge, Randolph County; *Phragmites communis*, Elk River, Randolph County, 1951; *Andropogon virginicus* var. *abbreviatus*, Elkins, 1959; *Asperula arvensis*, Bickle Knob road, 1959; *Carex stipata* var. *maxima* Elkins, 1959; *Stachys latidens*, near Elkins, 1958; *Echinops sphaerocephalus* near Elkins, 1960; and *Ornithogalum pyrenaicum* L., on the Bickle Knob road. The latter plant is new for North America. In recent years he has been studying the genera *Carex* and *Rubus* in Randolph County.

The publications of Dr. Hutton include the following:

The bog of Cranberry Flat, West Virginia. *Castanea* 6:18. 1941.

A *Carex* new to West Virginia. *Castanea* 6:144-145. 1941.

A botanist visits Tygarts Valley. *Mag. of Hist. and Biography of the Randolph Co. Hist. Soc.* 11:23-27. 1954.

(With R. B. Clarkson) Two plants new for North America and some new or otherwise interesting plants of West Virginia. *Castanea* 26:84-88. 1961.

Representatives of the circumpolar arctic flora in West Virginia, with special attention to Randolph County. *Wild Flower* 38:31-42. Oct. 1962.

William Clarence ("Bill") Legg was born October 18, 1903. He completed his formal education in the elementary and secondary schools of Nicholas County. He lived at Mt. Lookout, West Virginia, and operated a small-scale nature-publishing house, "Twintiliana Press," where he printed pamphlets to issue to his friends. He was a nationally known naturalist, and had been visited at his rural home by naturalists from many parts of the country as well as from some foreign countries. He provided materials and assistance for writings of nature authors, including Don Echelberry, of Long Island, N. Y., and at the time of his death had compiled notes for a book of his own.

A selection from one of his pamphlets, "Some Notes on Holly," published Feb. 5, 1947, illustrates his charming and informal style: "A holly is a sort of an apartment for myriads of insects. Some eat the leaf tissue between the leaf surfaces, some eat the bloom, the leaves, berries and many of them eat each other. As Fabre said, each is a guest and in turn the dish at the table of life. There's a balance here as in all Nature and the little black fly, *Phytomza ilicis*, whose grub mars the holly leaf with its mine, would increase this damage many fold were it not for a certain little wasp (*Braconid,* it seems) that preys on the fly. And I've seen this little wasp devoured by a larger insect (apparently a *Dolichopodidae*), which keeps its long abdomen curled up underneath itself. Conflicting with man's interest, *ilicis* is considered harmful, the other one beneficial, but there's no such distinction in Nature. They each fit the niche that they were adapted for. Like the hawk or an owl, they both fit perfectly in the niches they were created for. They know no other way than the beak and claw way so the gun has never 'educated' them to man's way.

"What has a hawk to do with holly? My alibi for this dissertation is probably that bugs eat holly, chickens eat bugs and hawks eat chickens." In speaking of this pamphlet he said "This is a very limited edition—in fact, so limited that it's about the same as talking to myself."

Many of his interesting collections of plants may be seen in the West Virginia University Herbarium. In his honor Dr. and Mrs. Davis named *Rubus leggii* (*Castanea* 18:27. 1953).

Mr. Legg died on May 30, 1952 near Summersville, as a result of a highway accident.

Henry Blair Graybill was born on October 22, 1880, in Amsterdam, Virginia, and died in Lewisburg, West Virginia, April 4, 1951. From 1902 until 1926 he served in various capacities on the staff of the Canton Christian College in Canton, China. He returned to the United States in 1926 and settled in Lewisburg. He spent the remainder of his life in that city, serving on the staffs of both Greenbrier College and the Greenbrier Military School in 1926-27, and from 1927 until his death remained at Greenbrier College, serving as professor of psychology and history.

Aside from his professional duties he found time to explore the outdoor world, and with long patience and investigation, prepared a check-list of the wild flowers of Greenbrier County.

Mrs. Kemble White was born June 24, 1877 in Greenville, South Carolina, and died at Clarksburg, West Virginia, March 19, 1941. She was president of the West Virginia Garden Club from its inception until her death, and a charter member of the Southern Appalachian Botanical Club. Her home, "Lilac Lodge," in Fairmont, West Virginia, was a show place for garden lovers, and her work with trees, shrubs, and flowers was recognized throughout the nation.

John Paul Tosh, while serving as a biology teacher in Woodrow Wilson High School, Beckley, West Virginia, in 1940-41 made a systematic survey of the vascular plants of Raleigh County, which served as a basis for a 107 page thesis submitted in partial fulfillment of the requirements for the degree of master of science at the University of Kentucky. Of the more than 800 species collected, several were new records for West Virginia, and most of them were the first authenticated records for Raleigh County. (See his "The vascular plants of Raleigh County." *Castanea* 7:55-70. 1942.)

Mildred (Cox) Blackburn Beals was born at Bethany, West Virginia, 1915. She received the bachelor of arts degree at West Liberty State College, and the master of arts degree at West Virginia University. She has had additional graduate training at West Virginia University, and Ohio State University.

Mrs. Beals is now a teacher of mathematics in Moundsville High School. During her teaching career she has made plant collections in Ohio, Brooke, Hancock, and Doddridge counties, and has contributed numerous specimens to the West Virginia University Herbarium. While serving as counselor at Camp Brookside, near Hinton, during the summer of 1958, she collected about 200 numbers, which were also donated to the University Herbarium.

REFERENCES

CHRISMAN, PATTIE H. "Hamilton McSparrin Gamble," *Castanea* 19:21-24. 1954.

CORE, EARL L. "Mrs. Kemble White," *Castanea* 6:88. 1941.

CORE, EARL L. "Henry Blair Graybill," *Castanea* 16:77-78. 1951.

CORE, EARL L. "Danske Dandridge," *Castanea* 16:138-142. 1951.

CORE, EARL L. "William Clarence Legg," *Castanea* 17:167. 1952.

CORE, EARL L., WILLIAM H. GILLESPIE AND BETTY J. GILLESPIE. Bibliography of West Virginia Plant Life. New York: Scholar's Library, 1962.

MORAN, REID. "Rufus Davis Alderson (1858-1932)," *Madroño* 16:224-228. 1962.

STRAUSBAUGH, P. D. "William Earl Rumsey," *Castanea* 3:53-54. 1938.

STRAUSBAUGH, P. D. "Rev. Fred W. Gray," *Castanea* 25:131-132. 1960.

CHAPTER XIV

The Study of Fungi[1]

BY C. R. ORTON

The history of a department is a record of events during the life of the department, which have influenced its development. It should include personnel, its activities, administration, cooperation, finances and effects on the general welfare.

The first publication from West Virginia University dealing with plant pathology was a brief description of some common diseases in *Bulletin* No. 21, April 1892, by A. D. Hopkins and C. F. Millspaugh under the title, "Injurious Insects and Plant Diseases."

The earliest experimental work in the field of plant pathology at West Virginia University was conducted by F. W. Rane, Horticulturist in the Agricultural Experiment Station, on the control of early blight of the potato and potato scab. It was found that three applications of Bordeaux Mixture controlled early blight on all but the most susceptible varieties, and that barnyard manure and lime applied to the soil increased scab, while soaking the seed tubers in corrosive sublimate reduced scab. (*Bulletin* 38, Nov. 1894.)

The systematic study of plant diseases at this Station may be said to have been initiated by J. L. Sheldon, who was Plant Pathologist and later Bacteriologist for the Station during the years 1903 to 1907. As plant pathologist in 1903, he was perhaps the first person to hold that title in the United States. Sheldon found that the anthracnose of watermelons was a serious disease in the Ohio Valley and by means of controlled experiments showed that the fungus from watermelon would infect cucumber, gourd and muskmelon, but neither squash nor pumpkin, nor wax beans. Spraying experiments with Soda-Bordeaux, Bordeaux, and ammoniacal copper carbonate, showed a decided decrease of the disease on blocks sprayed with the two Bordeaux mixtures, while plants sprayed with ammoniacal copper carbonate were not much better than the unsprayed plots. (Sheldon, J. L., "Muskmelon Blight." *West Virginia Agr.*

[1]The first portion of this chapter (pp. 156-166), by C. R. Orton, is reprinted by permission from *The Plant Disease Reporter*, Supplement 191, pp. 112-116. 1950.

Exp. Sta. Circ. 2. 1903; ibid., Bull. 94, Dec. 1904, "Diseases of Melons and Cucumbers," *West Virginia Agr. Exp. Sta.*)

Sheldon studied the ripe rot of guava, an important disease caused by *Glomerella psidii*, the perfect stage of which he discovered and fully described. (*Bull.* 104, Apr. 1906.)

During Dr. Sheldon's tenure a systematic attempt was made to collect and incorporate in a herbarium the parasitic fungi of the State. The collections were all studied carefully and accurately labeled. They form the basis of the known plant diseases of West Virginia. He published three accounts of his collections ("Report on Plant Diseases of the State." *West Virginia Agr. Exp. Sta. Rept.* 1903-04. 67-93. 1904; "A Report on Plant Diseases of the State." *West Virginia Agr. Exp. Sta. Bull.* 96. Jan. 1905; "The Principal Plant Diseases in 1906." *West Virginia Agr. Exp. Sta. Rept.* 1905-06:29-39, 1906).

Dr. Sheldon's last publication as a member of the Agricultural Experiment Station Staff appeared as Bulletin 105, June 1906, under the title "Tubercles on legumes with and without cultures." He was assisted in 1907 by Carl Hartley, a young graduate from the University of Nebraska. The following quotation from Dr. Hartley in a letter dated August 10, 1949, is interesting: "Charles E. Bessey sent me to West Virginia for my first job because of his high opinion of Sheldon as a teacher, which I can emphatically confirm."

Sheldon resigned from the Agricultural Experiment Station on June 30, 1907, when he was appointed Professor of Botany and Bacteriology in the College of Arts and Sciences. From that time until 1917, plant pathology and bacteriology were taught by Dr. Sheldon. He offered two courses, one an elementary course offered in the spring term; the other an advanced course offered throughout the year by special arrangement. Sheldon also taught, in addition to botany, three courses in bacteriology—general, agricultural and medical. In 1917 N. J. Giddings became a member of the Agricultural College faculty and offered his first course in plant pathology.

In the fall of 1908, N. J. Giddings, (Fig. 29), a graduate of the University of Vermont with a Master's degree, and, at that time, employed as Assistant Botanist of the Vermont Agricultural Experiment Station, was engaged as bacteriologist and assumed his duties at the West Virginia Agricultural Experiment Station on February 22, 1909. He was given quarters in the Northeast corner of the first floor of the old Experiment Station building. The facilities were restricted to a few test tubes, a Spencer microscope, herbarium, transfer room, and an old roll-top desk and chair.

This was a great transition from a well-equipped laboratory at Vermont, but Giddings attacked the problem with ability

Fig. 27. Ellis Meade McNeill

Fig. 28. Frederick William Gray

Fig. 29. Nahum James Giddings

Fig. 30. Julian Gilbert Leach

and enthusiasm and within a few years he secured equipment that surpassed that in the laboratories of many larger institutions.

The first assignment handed Giddings was the preparation of a station bulletin on "Diseases of Garden Crops and Their Control" which was published as *Bulletin* 123, May 1909. Regarding this, Giddings made the following comments: "Soon after it was published, F. C. Stewart of the Geneva, New York, Station wrote me expressing his opinion of young upstarts who wrote bulletins without any real knowledge of the problems existing in the area where he was located. Stewart was right and I wrote him to that effect, although the criticism did not make me any happier." To offset this discouragement he received a very kind and encouraging letter from Professor Charles Bessey, which was deeply appreciated.

As Giddings was employed as bacteriologist, his early research in the West Virginia Agricultural Experiment Station was in that field. He was assigned projects in cooperation with other members of the staff. The first was a study of the bacteria in milk, the results of which were published under the title "Experiments in the Production of Sanitary Milk" (Atwood, Horace, and N. J. Giddings. *West Virginia Agr. Exp. Sta. Bull.* 134, 1911). The second was upon the effects of high pressure on microorganisms in cooperation with B. H. Hite. This was pioneer research which resulted in the establishment of general principles upon which much of our present knowledge regarding the sterilization of food products is based. The work was published under the title, "The Effect of Pressure on Certain Microorganisms Encountered in the Preservation of Fruits and Vegetables" (B. H. Hite, N. J. Giddings and Charles E. Weakley, Jr., *West Virginia Agr. Exp. Sta. Bull.* 146, 1914). This work led later to the first proof that a virus could be inactivated by high pressures. In collaboration with Allard of the U. S. Department of Agriculture and with Hite, it was proved that tobacco mosaic was inactivated by pressure of 130,000 pounds and above (Giddings, N. J., H. A. Allard, and B. H. Hite, "Inactivation of the Tobacco Mosaic Virus by High Pressure." *Phytopathology* 9:1919).

Giddings carried over from his Vermont experience an interest in potato blights. It is not surprising, therefore, to find that he started potato spraying in 1909 which continued for several years. His first tests were at Morgantown, followed by plots at Reedsville and Moundsville. ("Potato Spraying in 1909 and

1910." *West Virginia Agr. Exp. Sta. Rept.* 1909-1910:18-22, 1910; "Potato Spraying Experiments in 1911." *West Virginia Agr. Exp. Sta. Rept.* 1911-12:77-78. 1912.) During these experiments, he developed a three-row boom with two nozzles at each row, illustrated in the 1909-10 report, p. 21.

In the fall of 1911, C. M. Gifford, a Vermont graduate, was appointed as assistant bacteriologist in the Station but, most unfortunately, he was drowned at Christmas time while skating on the Monongahela River.

In the fall of 1911, D. C. Neal, a graduate of Mississippi College of Agriculture and Mechanic Arts, was appointed Assistant Plant Pathologist. He assisted Giddings with the spray program for the control of apple rust and other apple diseases. He resigned March 1, 1914.

An important event occurred in 1912 when plant pathology was first recognized as a department in the Agricultural Experiment Station, and Giddings' title was changed from bacteriologist to plant pathologist (*W. Va. Agr. Exp. Sta. Rept.* 1911-12:54. 1912).

The year 1912 was a fruitful one for the Department. It may be called the period of national recognition. Giddings published his first two papers in *Phytopathology* that year—the first on "A Practical and Reliable Apparatus for Culture Work at Low Temperatures" (*Phytopath.* 2:106-190. 1912). This apparatus consisted of a standard incubator superimposed upon an icebox and equipped with thermo-regulator, small electric motor, rotary pump, and suitable copper piping. It worked. The second was a short paper by Giddings and Neal on "Control of Apple Rust by Spraying" in which they demonstrated that apple rust can be controlled with Bordeaux Mixture by the accurate timing of frequent applications at the critical periods of sporidial discharge (*Phytopath.* 2:258. 1912).

About the same time, the Department of Horticulture moved from the old Experiment Station Building into a temporary building (Oglebay Annex) and Plant Pathology was permitted to expand across the halls and to use the hallway to house the herbarium cabinets.

Additional funds were made available for the employment of another staff member, and Anthony Berg, a recent graduate from the University of Wisconsin, was appointed Assistant Plant Pathologist, March 15, 1913. Giddings and Berg made an excellent team and established plant pathological work at the West Virginia Agricultural Experiment Station on a sound basis, through their studies on apple rust. This problem had been of prime importance for many years in the Shenandoah Valley. It was estimated that rust caused a loss of $75,000 in one county in 1912. Work was begun on apple rust in 1910, but a formal project on apple rust was not initiated until 1913. It was continued until after Giddings resigned in 1929. Several noteworthy contributions to our knowledge of this disease were made during that period viz—"Apple Rust" by Giddings and Berg (*West Virginia Agr. Exp. Sta. Bull.* 154. 1915); "New or Noteworthy Facts Concerning Apple Rust" by Giddings and Berg (*Phytopath.* 6:79. 1916); and "Infection and immunity in Apple Rust" by Giddings (*West Virginia Agr. Expt. Sta. Bull.* 170, 1918), a classic study of this disease. It was Giddings' and Berg's practical demonstrations of the relation of the galls in the red cedars to the apple rust which played an important role in settling the law suits against the State for cutting the red cedars in proximity to apple orchards. Many worthy citizens in the Valley considered red cedars to be of more aesthetic value than the apple orchards. Berg also worked on rust resistance in the red cedar. He found an immune red cedar at Priest's Field in Jefferson County from which propogations by cuttings and grafts were made and distributed in other States, where it is known as "Berg's rust-resistant red cedar" (Anthony Berg. "A Rust Resistant Cedar." *Phytopath.* 30:876-878. 1940).

The chestnut blight was found in West Virginia about 1910, and investigations were begun in 1912 by A. B. Brooks, Forest Pathologist, employed jointly by the U. S. Department of Agriculture and the West Virginia Agricultural Experiment Station, with Giddings cooperating. Several acres of forest land were acquired by the State near Great Cacapon, on which a laboratory was established for the study of the blight. One bulletin was published by Giddings. ("Chestnut Bark Disease" *West Virginia Agr. Expt. Sta. Bull.* 137. 1912.)

"Collar blight" became recognized as an important disease of Grimes and certain other apple varieties early in the development of the apple industry in the Shenandoah Valley. Giddings carried on a rather intensive study on the control of this disease through surgical methods and inarching which saved many trees which would have died without such treatment ("The Collar Blight of Apple Trees" by N. J. Giddings, *West Virginia Dept. of Agr. Rept.* 29:15. 1913).

In 1909 and 1910 there were many reports of a serious disease of tomatoes in southern West Virginia. This problem was assigned to Berg, who proved that a strain of *Phytophthora infestans* was the cause. Berg's careful technique enabled him to culture the organism, prove its pathogenicity and establish its close relationship with the strain causing late blight of potatoes. The results were published under the title, "Tomato Late Blight and Its Relationship to Late Blight of Potato" (Giddings, N. J. and Anthony Berg, *West Virginia Agr. Expt. Sta. Bull.* 205. 1926; also *Phytopath.* 9:209-211. 1919).

In 1910, Mr. D. Gold Miller, a prominent orchardist in Berkeley County, sprayed a block of York Imperial apples with atomic sulfur, with the result that those trees were practically free from rust. This set Giddings to work on a comparison of dusting vs. spraying which continued for several years, during which time several States cooperated in comparative tests.

Three publications from the West Virginia Station resulted from this project (Giddings, N. J. "Orchard Spraying versus Dusting." *West Virginia Agr. Expt. Sta. Bull.* 167. 1918; Giddings, N. J. "Orchard Dusting versus Spraying." *Jour. Econ. Ent.* 14:225-231. 1921; Giddings, N. J., Anthony Berg and E. C. Sherwood. "Dusting and Spraying in the Apple Orchard." *West Virginia Agr. Expt. Sta. Bull.* 209. 1927).

The cooperative study with other States and Ontario was reported and published under the title "Cooperative Dusting and Spraying Experiments in 1921," and edited by C. R. Orton as a cooperative venture under the auspices of the Crop Protection Institute. (*C. P. I. Digest.* 1: No. 2, 1-30, 1922.) It was shown that dust fungicides were nearly as effective as sprays on peaches but not as effective as sprays on apple diseases, although dusts gave good commercial control of frog-eye leaf spot.

With the acquisition, in 1916, of farm land as a gift to the Agricultural Experiment Station from Monongalia County, the Department of Plant Pathology was assigned a tract adjacent to the Horticultural Farm. An experimental planting of apple trees for rust studies brought prompt and urgent protests which resulted in moving to a tract back of the Agronomy Farm. This area was developed as a pathologium which was actively used for experimental work until after Dr. Giddings resigned in 1929. Since then, it has been used primarily for the walnut canker and chestnut blight projects.

Potato Wart was discovered in Pennsylvania in 1918 and a year later in two localities in West Virginia in Grant and Tucker Counties, at relatively high altitudes. The scare caused by these discoveries persisted for several years, and quarantine regulations invoked at the time are still in force though the disease has not recurred for several years.

Oglebay Hall was erected in 1918, and Plant Pathology moved to the top floor of the new building along with Botany. This was a welcome change of quarters which was further improved in 1927 when Botany moved to Science Hall and Plant Pathology was given one office and the laboratory vacated by that department. Greenhouse space, which had always been a problem, was partially solved by the erection of a new greenhouse in 1920 for use by Botany and Plant Pathology.

The demand for plant pathological work was increasing and, on July 1, 1920, E. C. Sherwood, who had just completed work for the Master's degree at the University of Wisconsin, was appointed Extension Plant Pathologist, and Assistant Plant Pathologist in the Experiment Station. In July, 1926, he gave up his work in the Experiment Station and assumed half-time duties in regulatory work with the State Department of Agriculture. This arrangement was continued until his retirement in 1949. Sherwood's methodical approach to the practical control of orchard diseases and insect pests remains a standard of excellence as attested by the fruit growers of West Virginia and neighboring States. The annual control schedule published by Sherwood from the years 1926 to the present is a standard reference for the Shenandoah fruit-belt orchardists. Current issues appear under the title "Orchard Spraying Guide." Sherwood also published numerous special Extension circulars covering the diseases and insect pests of all cultivated crops.

An important addition to the staff was made in 1922 when L. H. Leonian,[2] fresh from his doctorate work in Kauffman's laboratory at Michigan, was appointed as Assistant Plant Pathologist. His enthusiasm, training, productivity, and *esprit de corps* were most valuable adjuncts in the further development of the department. His scientific contributions dealt with variability in the genera *Phytophthora* and *Fusarium*. For a time, he became interested in the fungi causing human diseases, but later concentrated his efforts in a study of the physiology of fungi with V. G. Lilly, a field which proved of special interest to him and in which he made notable progress. He became Professor of Mycology in 1936 and during the war years taught general bacteriology very successfully. Unfortunately, his career was untimely terminated by cancer which caused his death June 7, 1945.

[2]Born at Van, Armenia, February 27, 1888.

Late in the 1920's, reports of a new apple disease came in from several sections of the State. The disease resembled one which occurred in Arkansas and had been described by Hewitt of the Arkansas Agricultural Experiment Station as "measles." Mr. Berg was assigned to its study, and field work was initiated in Putnam County near Winfield, in Hancock County, and in Hampshire and Mineral Counties. The disease also became serious in Illinois, and specimens were received from several other States. Berg's studies soon led to the conclusion that more than one disease was involved in the "measles complex." He succeeded in isolating a *Helminthosporium* from the diseased trees at Winfield, which proved actively pathogenic. He named this disease "black pox" and described the pathogen under the name *H. papulosum.*

Giddings obtained a leave of absence in 1916-17 for graduate study at the University of Wisconsin, from which he obtained the doctorate in 1918. He remained head of the department until June 30, 1929, when he resigned to accept a position as Senior Pathologist in the U. S. Department of Agriculture. He has been stationed at Riverside, California, since that date.

The position thus vacated was filled by C. R. Orton, a graduate of the University of Vermont, with a Master's degree from Purdue University and his doctorate from Columbia University. At that time, Orton was engaged in research on seed disinfectants at the Boyce Thompson Institute, work financed at first by The Bayer Company, Inc., and later by the Bayer-Semesan Company. He had served previously for 12 years as Plant Pathologist at the Pennsylvania Agricultural Experiment Station and as Professor of Plant Pathology in the Pennsylvania State College.

The year 1930 may be termed the beginning of the period of graduate work in the department. Two graduate assistants were appointed that year—Joseph Myers Ashcroft and Bailey Sleeth, both graduates of West Virginia University, the latter having already taken his Master's at the University. Sleeth completed his work and received his doctorate in June 1932. His thesis was published in *Bulletin* No. 257 in 1934 under the title "*Fusarium niveum*, the Cause of Watermelon Wilt." Ashcroft completed his Master's degree in June 1931 and his Ph.D. in June 1933. His thesis "European Canker of Black Walnut and Other Hardwoods" was published as *Bulletin* No. 261, 1934. Up to the present time, 20 M.S. and 20 Ph.D. degrees have been earned in the Department.

Financial stringencies hit the State in 1933 when the Legislature cut the University appropriation heavily. President Turner advocated cutting overhead administrative expenses by merging related departments. An executive order was issued to Orton and Dr. P. D. Strausbaugh to study the possibility of merging all biological work excepting medicine, in a Department of Biology. A detailed report was made to the President, suggesting that Botany, Zoology, Bacteriology, Physiology, Forestry, and Plant Pathology could be organized in one department and all be housed, so far as possible, in Science Hall. This suggestion was approved by the Board of Governors and Orton was appointed head of a new Department of Biology to be administered in the College of Agriculture and Home Economics.

This was a major operation which involved moving Plant Pathology into the basement of Science Hall which, up to that time, had been used chiefly for storage. The move was made and the entire curriculum was revised. The transfer of Botany and Zoology from the College of Arts and Sciences into a department administered in the College of Agriculture was considered by some staff members to be a serious mistake. Administrative and personnel difficulties eventually led to the dissolution of the Department of Biology in 1936 during the presidency of Dr. Boucher. The Department of Plant Pathology emerged as a Department of Plant Pathology and Forestry, with Bacteriology included. Botany and Zoology were returned as a merged department to the College of Arts and Sciences. In the separation, Genevieve Clulo was transferred to the Department of Plant Pathology.

In 1938 Forestry was made a new division of the college and bacteriology was officially recognized in the reorganized Department of Plant Pathology and Bacteriology. In this year, Orton was appointed Dean and Director, and J. G. Leach,[3] a graduate of the University of Tennessee with a doctorate from Minnesota, and at that time Professor of Plant Pathology at Minnesota, was appointed Head of the Department. Eldor A. Marten (Ph.D., Wisconsin) was Associate Professor of Bacteriology from 1936 to 1941. He did research and published papers on soil microbiology, ring rot of potatoes, and factors influencing the toxicity of cuprous oxide. Marten was succeeded by Dr. A. R. Colmer (Ph.D., Wisconsin) who resigned in 1947. While at West Virginia, Dr. Colmer did research and

[3]Dr. Leach is author of the textbook, "Insect Transmission of Plant Diseases." McGraw-Hill, New York. 1940. 615 p. Portrait, Fig. 30.

published papers on the pasteurization of walnut meats and on the microbiology of acid mine waters. The work on mine water bacteria was revolutionary in nature and has contributed much to the important problem of stream pollution.

Dr. Colmer was succeeded in 1947 by Dr. H. A. Wilson (Ph.D., Iowa State College), and in 1948 an additional instructor in Bacteriology was added to the Department by the appointment of Mary Alice Ryan (M.S., West Virginia University).

Three members of the Department of Plant Pathology and Bacteriology have died in active service. Lawson M. Hill who with C. R. Orton made pioneer studies in purple-top wilt of potatoes, was appointed assistant in Plant Pathology in 1937 and died in 1939 while on leave of absence at the University of Arizona. Dr. Leonian, Professor of Mycology, who joined the staff in 1922, died in 1945 after 23 years of productive research in the physiology of the fungi. Anthony Berg, who joined the staff in 1913, died suddenly from a heart attack in 1947 after 34 years of service. He was a member of the department for a longer period of time than any other person.

RECENT DEVELOPMENTS

BY J. G. LEACH

During the next few years the work of the department was expanded and strengthened by the addition of several new staff members. In 1938, Dr. C. F. Taylor came from Cornell University to take charge of research and teaching in the field of fruit diseases and made many valuable contributions before leaving in 1956 to serve the Federal Government and later to join the Extension staff at Pennsylvania State University.

Service to the farmers of the state was expanded and strengthened in 1947 by the appointment of Dr. C. F. Bishop as Extension Plant Pathologist and Entomologist in which position he served with outstanding distinction until 1956 when he resigned to accept a position as Head of the Department of Biology at his *Alma Mater*, Goshen College.

In 1949, Dr. R. P. True (Ph.D., University of Pennsylvania), formerly with the U. S. Department of Agriculture, was appointed Associate Plant Pathologist in charge of research and instruction in forest pathology. In the same year, Dr. M. E. Gallegly (Ph.D., University of Wisconsin) was appointed Assistant Plant Pathologist in charge of work on diseases of potatoes and vegetables. Dr. True has become especially well known for his efficient direction of the oak-wilt research program in West Virginia, and Dr. Gallegly for his work on the late-blight disease of potato and tomato, having been the recipient in 1969, of the A.A.A.S.—Campbell Award of $1500 for outstanding contributions in the field of vegetable research.

Further extension took place in 1953 when Dr. E. S. Elliott was added to the staff as Assistant Plant Pathologist, in charge of diseases of forage crops and diseases of ornamental plants.

Dr. H. L. Barnett, a student of Ernst A. Bessey of Michigan State University, was appointed Mycologist to continue, in cooperation with Dr. V. G. Lilly, the work on the physiology of the fungi initiated and developed so effectively by Leonian and Lilly. This proved to be a happy choice for under the leadership of Drs. Lilly and Barnett, West Virginia University has gained an enviable international reputation as one of the strongest centers of research in this field.[4] In 1960, when J. G. Leach reached the age of administrative retirement, Dr. Barnett was selected as the new Chairman of the Department.

In 1945, Dr. Marten resigned to enter commercial work and Dr. Arthur B. Colmer was appointed to succeed him. The following year a new position in Bacteriology was created and Mary Alice Ryan was appointed Instructor in Bacteriology but resigned shortly thereafter. This position is now filled by Assistant Professor J. A. Koburger (Ph.D., North Carolina State). In 1947, Dr. Colmer resigned to accept a position at Louisiana State University. Although Dr. Colmer had remained with the Department only two years, he made important contributions to science and to the stream pollution problem by demonstrating that both the acidity and iron deposits of mine drainage were due to specific bacterial activity. Dr. H. A. Wilson replaced Dr. Colmer and has made important contributions to the microbiology of coal mine spoils.

The year 1950-1951 was a bright one for then the Department moved from the highly inadequate space in Science Hall to more modern quarters in Brooks Hall (which incidentally were outgrown in a few years).

In 1952, upon the retirement of Dr. L. M. Peairs, Head of the Department of Entomology, that department was merged with the Department of Plant Pathology, and Bacteriology. Dr.

[4]See their textbook, "The Physiology of the Fungi." McGraw-Hill, New York. 1951. 463 p. This book has also appeared in a Polish edition as: "Fizjologia Grzybow." 504 p. Warszawa. 1959.

C. K. Dorsey (Ph.D., University of Maryland) of Washington University was appointed Professor of Entomology.

The following year Dr. Robert Adams came from Cornell University as Assistant Professor of Plant Pathology, replacing Dr. Taylor, in charge of diseases of fruit crops. Dr. Adams soon became involved in research on nematodes and became very proficient in this field. After a short time he was relieved of other duties so that he, with the assistance of Mr. J. J. Eichenmuller, could devote full time to the study of nematodes as plant pathogens.

In 1956, David O. Quinn was appointed Extension Plant Pathologist and Entomologist replacing Dr. Bishop and two years later Dr. J. G. Barrett of the University of New Hampshire was appointed spray specialist for orchard fruits, taking over the service so ably carried out by Mr. Sherwood for many years.

In 1949, Dean Orton retired as Dean and Director and returned to the Department as Professor of Plant Pathology. He became engaged in research on internal bark necrosis of apple in association with Genevieve Clulo Berg who continued work on this disease after the death of her husband. In 1952, Mrs. Berg retired because of ill health and passed away three years later. In 1958, after the death of Dr. Orton (in 1955), the accumulated work on this puzzling disease was published posthumously as a technical bulletin.

Even this brief history of Plant Pathology in West Virginia would not be complete without mention of the control of plant diseases by legal regulatory measures and the cooperation of the various state and federal agencies involved. Such eradication and quarantine programs related to the control of apple rust (by cedar eradication), white pine blister rust (by *Ribes* eradication), and cereal rusts (by barberry eradication), not only have historical interest but have protected our state from serious crop losses from plant diseases. More recently but no less significant are the current efforts to control oak wilt on a state-wide basis.

Special credit for the efficiency of this disease control program is due to the splendid cooperation of Mr. Waldo Craig who has been responsible for this phase of the work of the West Virginia Department of Agriculture since 1926 and has been largely responsible for the formulation of policies and enforcement of the West Virginia Pest Control law first enacted in 1917.

Noteworthy has been the development of graduate instruction in Plant Pathology. The Plant Pathology Department has never offered an undergraduate major but was instrumental in providing an undergraduate curriculum in agricultural science primarily designed for the student who wished to prepare himself for graduate work in this or other fields within the area of agricultural science.

Graduate studies in plant pathology began with two students in 1930 and has shown steady growth until in 1962 there were a total of 26 graduate students enrolled in the department, 23 of whom were majoring in plant pathology or microbiology. In all a total of 52 M.S. degrees and 28 Ph.D. degrees in plant pathology or microbiology have been earned in the department.

The following members of the Plant Pathology Department have rendered service to their profession as officers of Professional Societies:

N. J. Giddings, Vice President, American Phytopathological Society, 1922.

C. R. Orton, President, American Phytopathological Society, 1939.

J. G. Leach, President, American Phytopathological Society, 1941.

————————, President, Potomac Division, American Phytopathological Society, 1956.

H. L. Barnett, President, Mycological Society of America, 1963.

————————, President, Potomac Division, American Phytopathological Society, 1963.

The following individuals were members of the department for relatively short periods of time:

Carl Hartley—Assistant in Plant Pathology—1907.

C. M. Gifford—Assistant Bacteriologist—1911.

D. C. Neal—Assistant Plant Pathologist—1911-1914.

Lawson M. Hill—Assistant in Plant Pathology—1939. Died in service.

John R. Vaughn—Extension Plant Pathologist—1941-1942.

Robert Atkinson—Extension Plant Pathologist—1941-1942.

John R. Fulkerson—Spray Specialist—1951-1953.

Mrs. Gwendolyn Stewart—Instructor in Bacteriology—1953-1955.

H. G. Hedrick—Instructor in Bacteriology—1955-1957.

H. L. Hansen—Assistant Professor of Entomology—1955-1958.

W. D. Schultze—Assistant Professor of Bacteriology—1958-1960.

H. M. Kulman—Assistant Professor of Entomology—1958-1962.

CHAPTER XV

Other Contributions

No attempt has been made to include an account of all the contributions to botany in West Virginia, but rather to weave the major botanical developments around educational institutions, and major personalities, "beacon lights," so to speak. However, botanists, amateur and professional, who have studied within our borders are worthy of mention.

Joseph E. Harned (1870-1951) was born at Oakland, Maryland, December 1, 1870. He graduated from the Philadelphia College of Pharmacy and of the sixty years that he practiced pharmacy all but two were spent at Oakland. He received the honorary doctor of science degree from both West Virginia Wesleyan College and Western Maryland College. He was a member of the American Association for the Advancement of Science, the Botanical Society of America, and the Southern Appalachian Botanical Club.

Dr. Harned was best known for his book "Wild Flowers of the Alleghenies," which was published in 1931.[1] In gathering information for the book he made numerous trips into West Virginia, resulting in the discovery of numerous species new for the State.

The true greatness of the man can be illustrated by the following appraisal of him before his death from an account written by Dale Carnegie and read during the funeral service:

> "His love for wild flowers has never deserted him. Sundays he tramped the flatlands of Maryland; he took trips into the mountains; he studied the wild flowers with breathless consuming interest. One day an idea stole into his mind as softly as a jack-in-the-pulpit pushing through the leaf mold. He would write a book on wild flowers. So he intensified his study. Finally the book was finished. He called it 'Wild Flowers of the Alleghenies.' A monumental book, superbly illustrated. One of the finest books ever written on wild flowers in the United States.

[1]See review of this book by Robert Sparks Walker in the Chattanooga *News*, August 27, 1934.

"Meantime Dr. Joseph E. Harned keeps right on running his pharmacy. In addition he goes out and makes speeches on wild flowers to schools and clubs. He wants to share his hobby every day with the public, so he places a vase of wild flowers on the counter of his store. Now and then someone asks him about the flowers. He is delighted. A smile comes into his face, his eyes take on a bright, shining light. Yes, indeed, Joseph E. Harned has one of the loveliest, most satisfying hobbies in all the world. He is a happy man because he has an enthusiasm for something beautiful outside himself. Something he can share with others."

Francis Welles Hunnewell, attorney and amateur botanist, was born at Boston, Massachusetts, December 28, 1880. He attended Harvard University, receiving the bachelor of arts degree in 1902, the bachelor of law degree in 1905, and the master of arts (honorary) in 1934.

His collections, including hundreds of specimens gathered on many trips into the mountains of West Virginia, are mostly in the New England Botanical Club Herbarium, the Gray Herbarium, and the Herbarium of West Virginia University. (See his, "*Botrychium matricariaefolium* in West Virginia" *Castanea* 13:93. 1948, and "New plant records for West Virginia" *Castanea* 16:63-64. 1951.)

Raymond H. Torrey was born July 15, 1880 and died at his home in New York, N. Y., on his 58th birthday. He was a member of the Torrey Botanical Club (which was named in honor of John Torrey, a remote relative of his), and served for many years as chairman of the club's field committee, and at the time of his death was serving as president. He was an original member of the Southern Appalachian Botanical Club, and occasionally came into the Southern Appalachian region, when he and Dr. Core arranged several intersectional forays. As a journalist by profession he served at one time as night city editor of the New York *American* and later of the New York *Tribune*. In the late years of his life his writings were confined mainly to a column in the New York *Post* entitled "The Long Brown Path," which was a clearing house of information for naturalists and hikers. He was intensely interested in lichens, and especially in the genus *Cladonia*. (See biography by James Murphy, *Bull. Torr. Bot. Club* 65:433-438. 1938.)

Mrs. N. L. Britton (Elizabeth Gertrude Britton) in August, 1890, collected a number of mosses in the vicinity of

White Sulphur Springs. These are deposited in the Elizabeth Gertrude Britton Moss Herbarium of the New York Botanical Garden.

Andrew Delmar Hopkins (1857-1948), forest entomologist of the United States Department of Agriculture, collected unusual plants in various parts of the state from 1892 to 1902, while pursuing his entomological studies, depositing them in the West Virginia Agricultural Experiment Station Herbarium while he was vice-director of the Station. This collection is now incorporated in the University Herbarium.

Amos Arthur Heller, of the University of Nevada, did considerable collecting on Kate's Mountain and in the vicinity of White Sulphur Springs in 1893. A set of his plants was deposited in the Field Museum of Natural History Herbarium.

Lee Cleveland Corbett, while engaged in forest field work for the West Virginia Agricultural Experiment Station, collected a number of plants from 1894 to 1896, depositing them in the herbarium of the Station. (See his "Cranberries in West Virginia," *W. Va. Agri. Exp. Sta., Bull.* 86:115-126. 1903.)

William McCalley Pollock, while a student at West Virginia University, collected largely from 1893 to 1897, in Lewis, Upshur, Preston, Pocahontas, Taylor and Wood Counties, and in 1898 to 1899 in Monongalia County. His prime series of about 1,700 specimens was accidentally destroyed.

Rev. A. Boutlou, of Fairmont, spent considerable of his spare time from 1897 to 1907 botanizing in Marion, Taylor, Monongalia, and Preston counties.

Edward Lee Greene, of the National Herbarium, spent a day or so once or twice each year from 1897 to 1912 in the vicinity of Harpers Ferry. His collecting in this region was of a highly discriminating character, confined to such plants as appeared to differ from the usual form. One of his collections, at Harpers Ferry, May 14, 1898, was described as a new species, *Antennaria propinqua* Greene (*Pittonia* 4:83. 1899). His specimens are in the National Herbarium.

Edward Strieby Steele (born April 20, 1850 near Farmingdale, Illinois; died January 3, 1942), of the U. S. Department of Agriculture, with the aid of Mrs. Steele, spent several days in August and September, 1898, collecting in the neighborhood of Aurora, Preston County. He secured about 325 numbers, which were deposited in the National Herbarium. In 1903 and again in 1905 he collected near Old Sweet Springs in Monroe County, and in 1906 at White Sulphur Springs. In 1910 he collected a few specimens in Grant County and in 1911 in Hardy County. These later collections are also in the National Herbarium, with hundreds of duplicates in the Herbarium of West Virginia University. (See his "New or Noteworthy Plants from the Eastern United States," *Contrib. U. S. Natl. Herb.* 12:359-374. 1911.)

Plants named for Mr. Steele are as follows: *Liatris steelei* Gaiser, *Rubus steelei* Bailey, *Aster steeleorum* Shinners, and *Thalictrum steeleanum* Boivin.

Charles Louis Pollard and **William Ralph Maxon** collected in August, 1899, near Quinnimont, in Fayette County, and near Lowell in Summers County. About 30 of the 125 numbers were new to the state. Their plants are deposited in the National Herbarium. (See "Some new and additional records of the flora of West Virginia," *Proc. Biol. Soc. Wash.* 14:161-163. 1901; also "Notes on American ferns," *Am. Fern Jour.* 9:1-5. 1919.)

Edward Lyman Morris, curator of the Brooklyn Institute Museum, while engaged in field work for the U. S. Fish Commission in 1900, made a collection of plants in the region lying south of the New, Greenbrier, and Kanawha rivers in Summers, Monroe, Mercer, McDowell, Raleigh, and Wyoming counties. His collection of 397 numbers is in the National Herbarium. (See his "Some Plants of West Virginia," *Bull. Biol. Soc. Wash.* 13:171-182. 1900.)

Henry Curtis Beardslee spent the summer of 1900 collecting mainly fleshy fungi in the vicinity of Brookside, Preston County. His collection consisted of about 600 specimens. (See his "Notes on the Boleti of West Virginia," *Torreya* 1:37-39. 1901.)

Curtis Gates Lloyd of the Lloyd Herbarium, Cincinnati, Ohio, collected for about two weeks at Eglon, Preston County, in 1901. His specimens, chiefly fungi, are preserved in the Lloyd Herbarium at Cincinnati.

William Ashbrook Kellerman, professor of botany at Ohio State University, collected principally fungi, at Durbin and Marlinton in August, 1902.

Albert Spear Hitchcock, agrostologist of the U. S. Department of Agriculture, made small but discriminative collections, mostly of grasses, in the vicinity of Morgantown in 1902 and in 1929, and Harpers Ferry in 1905. His plants are in the National Herbarium, with some duplicates in the Herbarium of West Virginia University.

Charles L. Boynton, of the Biltmore Herbarium, collected in June, 1903, at Huntington, Kenova, Milton, St. Albans, Salters, Charleston, Eastbank, Gauley Bridge, Thurmond, Hinton, and White Sulphur Springs, revisiting the latter place in October. In May and September, 1904 he again collected in the neighborhood of White Sulphur Springs. His collection of 295 numbers is in the National Herbarium.

Albert LeRoy Andrews, while connected with West Virginia University in 1903 and 1904, collected in many localities in Monongalia and Preston counties, specializing in the bryophytes. His plants are in the herbaria of West Virginia University and Williams College, and in his private herbarium. (See his "Additions to the Bryophytic Flora of West Virginia," *Bryologist* 8:63-65. 1905.)

Jesse Moore Greenman, curator of the herbarium, Missouri Botanical Garden, spent the month of September, 1904, collecting at the following places: Parsons and Hendricks in Tucker County; Spruce Knob in Pendleton County; Dry Fork, Horton, Elkins, Reedy, Whitman, Glady, Harman, and Huttonsville in Randolph County; Travelers Repose in Pocahontas County. The prime set of his collections, consisting of 1,500 specimens, is deposited in the Gray Herbarium.

Frank Fitch Grout, while connected with the West Virginia Geological Survey, collected a number of plants, especially parasitic fungi, from various parts of the state from 1904 to 1906. His collections are in the West Virginia University Herbarium.

Huron Herbert Smith, while assistant in dendrology at the Field Museum of Natural History, collected 246 numbers in Randolph, Webster, Nicholas, Lewis, Upshur, and Wood counties, in 1908. His specimens are deposited in the herbarium of the Museum.

Otto Emery Jennings, (born October 3, 1878), curator of botany at the Carnegie Museum, Pittsburgh, collected in West Virginia numerous times starting in 1909. His specimens are deposited in the herbarium of Carnegie Museum. See his "Wild Flowers of Western Pennsylvania and the Upper Ohio Basin." 2 vols. folio. Watercolors by Andrey Avinoff. Pittsburgh. 1953. Dr. Jennings died January 29, 1964.

William Webster Eggleston collected from 1909 to 1911,

with a view of securing all possible material in the Pomeae, gathering also a considerable number of other plants that appeared to be of particular interest. In 1909 he collected at White Sulphur Springs, Gauley Bridge, Thurmond, and Hinton. He collected again at White Sulphur Springs in 1911. His material is deposited in the herbarium of the New York Botanical Garden.

Per Axel Rydberg, of the New York Botanical Garden, collected through the Southern Appalachians in 1925, visiting Spruce Knob and Snowy Mountain, in Pendleton County. His collection of especially interesting forms is in the herbarium of the New York Botanical Garden. (See his "Botanizing in the Higher Allegheny Mountains, I. West Virginia," *Jour. N. Y. Bot. Gard.* 27:1-6. 1926; "Two new species from the mountains of West Virginia," *Torreya* 26:29-33. 1926.) New species discovered by him in West Virginia include *Aconitum vaccarum* and *Heuchera alba.*

Charles Alfred Weatherby, of the Gray Herbarium, in May 1933, collected 37 numbers in Greenbrier, Fayette, Pocahontas, and Randolph counties. His material is in the Gray Herbarium.

Francis Whittier Pennell, Curator of Botany, Philadelphia Academy of Sciences, while working on the Scrophulariaceae of eastern North America, made several collecting trips in West Virginia. His collections are in the herbarium of the Academy, with many duplicates in the West Virginia University Herbarium.

Mrs. Jane S. Netting, while accompanying her husband, Dr. Graham Netting, herpetologist at the Carnegie Museum (and later director), on collecting trips in West Virginia, discovered numerous new records for plants. (See her "A second record for *Listera smallii* Wiegand in West Virginia," *Torreya* 32:72. 1932.)

Clinton C. Taylor during the late summer of 1933 made a survey of the flora of Mineral County. His collection of 150 specimens is in the University Herbarium.

William W. Webb, formerly of Wheeling, made careful and discriminating collections of bryophytes, presenting them to the West Virginia University Herbarium in 1931.

Russell West, of Wheeling, in 1931 and afterwards played an important part in the exploration of the flora of the northern panhandle, in connection with the organization and development of the Oglebay Club. His collections are in the West Virginia University Herbarium. (See his "The Oglebay Plant Club." *Jour. So. Appalach. Bot. Club* (now *Castanea*) 1:8-9. 1936.)

Asa Howard Anderson and **Freeman Paul Smith** collected about 350 numbers of plants from Monongalia County during the summer of 1933, depositing them in the West Virginia University Herbarium.

W. J. Judy, while a teacher in Clarksburg High School, in 1934, made a study of the plants of the surroundings of Clarksburg, depositing 162 numbers in the West Virginia University Herbarium.

Charles Gould, Jr. made a survey of the polypores of the southwestern counties in 1934-35. Duplicates of his prime set were deposited in the Marshall College Herbarium and the West Virginia University Herbarium. (See his "Some Polyporaceae of southern West Virginia." *Proc. W. Va. Acad. Sci.* 9:25-28. 1936.)

Frank Cutright, while serving as professor of biology at Concord College, made collections of interesting plants in his locality, depositing them in the Concord College Herbarium and West Virginia University Herbarium.

Ben R. Roller (1880-1952), while serving as an Episcopal minister at White Sulphur Springs, made some interesting discoveries in the Alleghenies in that vicinity. (See his "Showy lady's slipper in West Virginia." *Castanea* 1:9-10. 1936.)

Paul Cecil Bibbee, formerly professor of biology at Concord College and now of Davis and Elkins College has made collections near his former home at Hanna and elsewhere, especially in the mountain counties.

Cora Burdette collected several numbers in 1943 in the vicinity of Organ Cave in Greenbrier County, depositing them in the West Virginia University Herbarium.

Carroll Smithson, while a forestry student at West Virginia University in 1936, collected several interesting specimens in Cabell County. Later, while connected with forestry work in the state, he made discriminating collections in Greenbrier and surrounding counties. His collections are filed in the West Virginia University Herbarium.

George H. Breiding, while a member of the staff of Oglebay Institute, Wheeling, West Virginia, studied the flora of the area, making interesting observations. (See his "Rock breakers." *W. Va. Conservation* 18(5):5. 1954; "A new plant for West Virginia." *Castanea* 20:132. 1955; "The Dutchman's pipe." *W. Va. Conservation* 19(4):18. 1955.) He became a member of the faculty of West Virginia University in 1963.

Aaron John Sharp (born July 29, 1904) of the University of Tennessee, was instructor in botany at West Virginia University during the summers of 1939-41. During this time he made numerous plant collections, including the type specimen of a *Rubus* named by L. H. Bailey for him, *R. sharpii* (*Gentes* Herbarum 5:420. 1943), from Cranesville, and another from Canaan Valley named by Dr. Bailey *R. discretus* (*Gentes Herbarum* 5:172. 1941).

Harry A. Allard was born at Oxford, Mass., January 28, 1880, and was graduated from the University of North Carolina with the degree of Bachelor of Science after specializing in botany and geology. Practically all of his professional career was spent in the U. S. Department of Agriculture, where, in connection with W. W. Garner, he became widely known through discovery of the law of photoperiodism, namely, that the flowering and fruiting of plants depends upon the length of the day or night.[2] The record of his more than 200 published papers shows a great variety of topics of interest to naturalists, including such subjects as toads, turtles, birds, springs, streams, soils, sounds, leaves, berries, crickets, firefly-flashing impulse, snakes, and plants. For many years he spent his vacations near Davis, in Tucker County, and collected a vast amount of information on the flora of Canaan Valley and the surrounding territory, publishing his results, in conjunction with E. C. Leonard, in a paper, "The Canaan and Stony River Valleys of West Virginia, their former magnificent spruce forests, their vegetation and floristics today." (*Castanea* 17:1-60. 1952). Among plants named for him are *Ruellia allardii* Leonard, *R. gudrifaria* var. *allardii* Leonard, *Viola allardii* Greene, *Lactarius allardii* Ckper., and *Septoria allardii* Stevenson and Pollack. He died February 25, 1963.

Rufus M. Reed, a nature writer of Lovely, Kentucky, has for several years written an outdoor column appearing in several newspapers of southern West Virginia. He has made several interesting botanical discoveries in the general area of Williamson. (See his "The *Mimosa* as an escape in West Virginia

[2]"Effect of the relative length of day and night and other factors of the environment on growth and reproduction in plants." *Jour. Agr. Res.* 18:64-79. 1920.

and Kentucky." *Castanea* 24:55-56. 1959; "Pluchea camphorata, a rare plant in southern West Virginia and eastern Kentucky." *Castanea* 25:129, 130. 1960.)

Attention should be given to the innumerable mountaineer plantsmen, mostly unversed in "book larnin," but none-the-less possessing a genuine love of plants and an accurate practical knowledge of them. Among these, perhaps no one was better known than **Moses** ("Mosey") **Randolph Bennett** (died October 15, 1949) who for many years was "top" man in West Virginia, living in a well-built home near the summit of Spruce Knob,

"And from Mt. Pisgah's lofty height
Brings forth his lens and takes a sight,"

like his illustrious namesake of old. Dr. Rydberg visited him on his trip to West Virginia in 1925 and noted that *Aconitum vaccarum* Rydberg was "originally discovered by U. S. Forest Ranger Moses Bennett." (See W. A. Dayton, "Moses Bennett's Baneful Monkshood" U. S. D. A. *Forest Service, Eastern District Digest,* April 28, 1926; a reprint is in the Archives of the West Virginia University Library.)

Credit should be given to the many individuals who study plants by the use of photography, building up slide and film collections. For many years these photographs, of course, were in black-and-white only, but were none the less valuable, preserving features of the primeval flora; the collections of W. E. Rumsey and the Brooks brothers are noteworthy. With the advent of color film the number of persons interested in nature photography increased greatly. Prominent among these individuals is **H. P. Sturm,** of Clarksburg, West Virginia. He has prepared the following sound motion pictures, in color, dealing with the plant life of West Virginia:

Plants of Appalachian Mountain Bogs. 1948. 10 min.

Plants of the Appalachian Shale Barrens. 1948. 11 min.

Wild Flowers of the Alleghenies. 1949. 45 min.

A Wild Orchid Pilgrimage. 1953. 35 min.

Carnivorous Plants (in preparation).

Other individuals who have also made significant contributions are **W. R. Lenhart**, of Morgantown, and **L. C. McDowell**, of Charleston. These men have each contributed hundreds of kodaslides to the large collection of plant photographs maintained at West Virginia University.

A recent development in the history of botany in West Virginia was the First Annual Wildflower Pilgrimage, held on May 15-18, 1962, at Blackwater Falls State Park, with 141 persons in attendance. Credit for this important botanical development should go to the Raleigh County Garden Council and its leader, **Mrs. Robert B. Parker**, of Glen White. Assistance with the Pilgrimage was furnished by the Department of Biology of West Virginia University and the West Virginia Department of Natural Resources. Dr. Earl L. Core, of West Virginia University, and Dr. A. J. Sharp, of the Department of Botany of the University of Tennessee, two authorities on the flora of the Appalachians, were on hand to assist. (See Blizzard, William C., 1962, "The cranny probers." W. Va. Conservation 26 [5]:21-27.) (The second annual pilgrimage was held May 15-18, 1963, and the third May 15-17, 1964, with over 200 persons attending.)

Fig. 31. Verona Mapel

PALEOBOTANY[3]

The name of the first person to find fossil plants in what is now West Virginia will probably never be known. The first published reference to a specific plant fossil that may have been collected within the present boundaries of West Virginia is contained in an article published by Dr. Richard Harlan in 1834, in which he describes his *Fucoides Brongniartii* as being collected in the "mountains of western Virginia".

The first important paper on the geology and paleobotany of our present West Virginia was published in 1836 by Drs. S. P. Hildreth and S. G. Morton of Marietta, Ohio. This paper embodied the observations and collections made by Dr. Hildreth, one of the first members of the Ohio Geological Survey, while he was studying the natural history of the Ohio Valley and adjacent territories. Twenty-five of the thirty-six plates in the appendix are mostly fossil plants collected by Hildreth and sketched and identified by Morton after comparison with existing European works.

A majority of the West Virginia specimens were collected from the roof shales of coal seams near Charleston, the present State Capital, which were mined as fuel for the "Kenawha [*sic*] salines". Hildreth stated that he found good compressions about 3½ miles above Charleston where coal (now identified as the Coalburg seam) was mined for the Daniel Boone Salt Works. He stated that other nice fossils were found where the same coal was mined for the Snow Hill salt works. The seams now known as the Winifrede and the Cedar Grove were also noted for fossils.[4]

A "Mrs. Brigham" of Charleston sketched a few figures for Hildreth's paper, and thus qualifies as one of the earlier illustrators in this country.

Dr. Morton states in the foreword to the appendix that the remains were "compared with the figures given by Sternberg, Brongniart and Lindley, but in many instances without success". Thus, the first important work describing fossil plants from West Virginia indicated the presence of previously undescribed forms—many of which were later to serve as type

[3]This account is reprinted by permission from W. H. Gillespie and I. S. Latimer, Jr., "History and Bibliography of West Virginia Paleobotany." *Castanea* 26:157-171. 1961.

[4]An interesting account of a recent find of fossil logs in the Charleston area is given by Swetnam (1953). The trees, found near a locality mentioned by Hildreth, were uncovered in a coal stripping operation, and now reside in the Carnegie Museum in Pittsburgh, Pennsylvania.

specimens. It is surprising that such an erudite paper appeared at such an early date, because the initial efforts in scientific paleobotany date back no farther than the beginning of the 19th century, as previously discussed. Ebenezer Granger's paper,[5] which is generally conceded to illustrate the first plant fossils from America, did not appear until 1821.

The collecting of fossil plants in the early 1800's was usually, as today, associated with geological and mining activities. Although geologists and engineers seldom publish their observations, they quite often directed important specimens to specialists. Such a man was William B. Rogers, who was the first to map the essential geologic features of the Kanawha Valley. He mentions several places in his report encountering "fossil plant horizons of exceptional beauty."[6]

After the initial work, paleobotanical studies of West Virginia specimens were rare. In fact, these early papers are apparently the only ones which appeared prior to the three contributions of Leo Lesquereux, the acknowledged "Father of American Paleobotany", which appeared in H. D. Rogers' work *The Geology of Pennsylvania.*[7] A brief outline of the events leading up to these papers is perhaps worthwhile.

Leo Lesquereux was born in Switzerland in 1806. As a young man he began to have hearing difficulties and consulted a specialist, but the ensuing treatments were so harsh they rendered him deaf for the remainder of his life. This, however, did not keep him from communicating with the world, as he trained himself to read lips in three languages—a really magnificent accomplishment. He avidly pursued a botanical education, the first dividend being a competitive prize for the best essay dealing with the formation of peat bogs. After one or two minor political appointments, he came to America, arriving in Boston in the mid-1840's. He first supported himself by identifying plants collected by Louis Agassiz, after which he collaborated with William Sullivant to produce the epic *Musci Exsiccati Americana.*

Paleobotany, as such, apparently played a very minor role in his life until 1851, when he was employed by the Pennsyl-

[5]Granger, Ebenezer. 1821. Notice of vegetable impressions on the rocks connected with the coal formations of Zanesville, Ohio. Amer. Journal of Science & Arts, New Haven. Vol. 3, page 5. Plates 1 and 2.

[6]Rogers, William B. 1884. Geology of the Virginias. N. Y. (The field work was finished in 1841 and a report was made to the Virginia legislature in 1846. This report was then printed as a book in 1884.)

[7]Rogers, H. D. 1858. The Geology of Pennsylvania. 3 Vols. Harrisburg.

vania Geological Survey to investigate and describe the coal flora of that State. His first two papers appeared in 1854 and 1858, but it is in Volume II, Part 2, of Roger's *Geology of Pennsylvania* that the first mention of fossil remains from West Virginia is made. His contribution to this work forms three articles in which he attempts to name and illustrate not only the coal flora of Pennsylvania, but also the entire known Carboniferous flora of the United States.

In this work he mentions the "Kenawha [*sic*] salines", where several new species had been collected. Many of the fossils described in this volume were donated by Dr. S. P. Hildreth of Marietta, Ohio, but there is no doubt but that Lesquereux himself also visited the localities. On page 839 he states,

> "The last place we had an opportunity to describe this vein, so rich in fossil plants, was at Great Kenawha [*sic*] River 3 miles above Charleston, and there we found the roof shales covered with *Alethopteris serlii*, with some fine *Lepidodendra*, and *Lepidostrobi* in abundance".

He also mentions, on page 840, the many large specimens of *Psaronius* noted at Athens, Ohio and Charlestown (Charleston), Virginia. A statement in the *American Naturalist* (vol. 5, p. 352, 1871) also concerns the large numbers of *Psaronius* along the Great Kenawha [*sic*] up to Charleston:

> " . . . silicified trunks washed from the Mahoning sandstone . . . from Athens southward, to the Ohio River, and in Virginia, as far up the Great Kenawha [*sic*] River as Charleston, or about 100 miles in a direct line".

Lesquereux's most monumental work, *The Coal Flora of the Carboniferous in Pennsylvania and the United States*, although outdated, is still the most remarkable publication on the subject in North America. The first two volumes, bound in one, and accompanied by an atlas of 85 double lithographic plates, appeared in 1880 and contained the results of all previous researches. The third and last volume was published in 1884 and contained a revision of the previous volumes plus all of the additional information that the author could muster. Several of the 835 species described in this work were originally collected in West Virginia.

During the period from 1858 to 1868, only one paper appeared that was even closely applicable to Western Virginia. James P. Kimball, of Massachusetts, prepared a doctoral dissertation at the University of Gottingen in 1857 entitled *Flora from the Appalachian Coal Fields*, based upon specimens collected by F. Roemer. It is noted that the fossil material was collected in Ohio and Pennsylvania; however, exact localities are not given, and it is probable that some of the specimens were from areas in close proximity to the borders of Western Virginia.

John James Stevenson (1841-1924) collected some fossils in connection with his general stratigraphic work, much of which was in West Virginia, during the period 1871-1881. He did not publish descriptive papers. Instead he referred his material to others, being content to mention the several collecting horizons in his geologic reports.

William Henry Edwards (1822-1909), superintendent of the Kanawha and Ohio Coal Company in Kanawha County, was an avid amateur collector. This lawyer and Amazon explorer, turned-miner, was much better known for the three editions of his book *The Butterflies of North America.* His personal collection was apparently lost, but it is recorded that he sent *Bothrodendron* specimens to both Lesquereux and to the Smithsonian Institution.

William Morris Fontaine (1835-1913), Professor of Chemistry and Geology at West Virginia University from 1873 to 1878 and Professor of Geology at the University of Virginia from 1878 until 1911, was an avid student of fossil floras. His work on the Mesozoic floras of Virginia is well-known, but his most illustrious work, and one which is still a center of controversy, was co-authored with Israel Charles White (1848-1927), then Professor of Geology at West Virginia University (1877-1892) and later West Virginia State Geologist (1897-1927). This small volume, entitled *The Permian or Upper Carboniferous Flora of West Virginia and Southwest Pennsylvania,* was completed in 1878 and issued in 1880. By far the greater part of the plants described were from the roof shales of a limited area in a Waynesburg coal drift mine at Cassville, Monongalia County, and similar material at West Union, Doddridge County. (This latter locality has been correlated as the Uniontown coal of slightly older age by more recent workers.) One hundred and eight species, of which 78 were new, were described from 14 localities at five different horizons. Their conclusions were that the many new species, along with *Callipteris,* usually regarded as an indicator of Permian age, and a ginkgo-like leaf named *Saportea,* constituted proof of the Permian age of the sediments. Most American geologists regarded the work as inconclusive, but Professor White stoutly defended the Permian position in several lectures and papers. His main thesis was that the transitional Permo-Carboniferous started with the red beds of the Conemaugh series, and that true Permian sediments occupied the 1,200 feet of strata above the Waynesburg coal horizon. Unfortunately, the specimens upon which this work was based were destroyed by a fire at the University of Virginia. Many of them have never been re-collected.

Dr. David White (1862-1935), one of America's leading paleobotanists of the time, collected at some of the Dunkard horizons in company with I. C. White in 1902. He reported[8] that the sediments above the Washington coal horizon are probably of Permian age, but that available evidence did not substantiate this age for lower strata, thus suppressing portions of the theory, but leaving the main question open to further proof.

Dr. Aureal T. Cross, after several years of intensive study, reported[9] that several of the new species described by Fontaine and White were probably different leaf forms of a few species. He stated that the 72 different species of *Pecopteris* would fall into about 12 natural species.

Recent workers have not found *Callipteris, Baiera, Saportea,* or many of the other fossils described in the original paper. In fact, Cross mentions finding dissected cyclopteroid pinnules that are the same in form and appearance as Fontaine and White's *Baiera* and *Saportea*, and suggests that these genera may be relegated to a status of *incertae sedis*.

Since none of the more recent workers have, as yet, published the results of their critical studies, Dr. White's system of classification—dating the Dunkard series as Permian—will have to stand for the present.

The famous Cassville Plant Shale, from which many of the specimens of Fontaine and White were collected, has often been the center of discussion. Down through the years, the idea has developed that their specimens were collected not from the roof shales, but from the clay parting which separates different benches of the coal. The authors, however, specifically state that the flora of the parting is almost exclusively *Alethopteris virginiana*, whereas the more varied flora occurs in "the roof-shales some distance above this variable parting." Recent

[8]"Permian elements in the Dunkard flora." (abs.) *Bull. Geol. Soc. Amer.* 14:539-542. 1904. *Jour. Geol.* 11:105, 106. 1903. *Science,* n.s., 17:298. 1903.

[9]"Fossil flora of the Dunkard strata of the eastern United States." *In* Sturgeon, "The geology and mineral resources of Athens County, Ohio." *Ohio Div. Geol. Surv. Bull.* 57, pp. 191-196. 1958.

collecting near the type area supports the original statement, although additional genera are found in the parting at other localities.

Professor Fontaine described several other important plants and localities in papers published in 1884 and 1886.

Frank H. Knowlton, another eminent paleobotanist of this period, apparently did not do much, if any, collecting within the State, but a collection of plant compressions from a terrace deposit near Morgantown, Monongalia County, West Virginia was referred to him for study. His identifications appeared in a paper published in 1896.

David White, an ardent student of Carboniferous compression floras, is regarded as one of the finest paleobotanists that America ever produced. He did extensive field work in West Virginia during the years 1886 to 1894, with several trips at later dates. His work here formed a basis for several publications. Some of these papers still remain as the only source of information available to modern workers, as, for example, his description of the Mississippian flora in the Appalachian Trough and his *Fossil Flora of West Virginia*, published in 1913. He was a successful advocate of using megafloras as stratigraphic aids. His study of the Dunkard has already been mentioned, and his papers on the fossil floras of Pennsylvania and Missouri are classics of their kind.

One of the more interesting problems involving David White was the controversy concerning the age and correlations of the coals in the Kanawha Valley. I. C. White correlated these coals, on stratigraphic evidence, with coals of the Allegheny Series in Pennsylvania. David White, on paleobotanical evidence, decided that these coals were older and correlated them with the Pottsville coals of Pennsylvania.

The controversy, carried on in miscellaneous scientific publications, was thoroughly reviewed by I. C. White in 1903 when he acknowledged that David White might be correct. Later, in 1908, I. C. White accepted David White's conclusions and placed the major group of the Kanawha coals in the Upper Pottsville, where they still remain.

Several of David White's collections are, as yet, unstudied due to the press of administrative duties during his later years when he was promoted to Chief Geologist of the United States Geological Survey. His last memorable visit to West Virginia, for strictly professional duties, was in 1927 when he gave a week of special lectures in the Geology Department of West Virginia University.

The first extensive listing of the fossil plants of West Virginia appeared in C. F. Millspaugh's *Preliminary Catalog of the Flora of West Virginia*, published by the West Virginia Agricultural Experiment Station in 1892. This supplement, contributed by R. D. Lacoe of Pittston, Pennsylvania, was based upon published works and upon specimens identified by Lacoe and by Lesquereux in his last years. Lacoe was one of paleobotany's foremost patrons and collectors. His interests were not confined to fossil plants, for the fossil cockroaches described by Scudder[10] from the Waynesburg coal horizon were collected by C. L. Eakin of Blacksville, Monongalia County, through the financial generosity of Lacoe.

Charles Arthur Hollick was another of the geologist-paleobotanists to whom specimens were often referred. He published at least one paper[11] based upon West Virginia material.

David Bright Reger, Assistant Geologist with the West Virginia Geological and Economic Survey from 1911 to 1930, collected fossil plants from several dozen horizons while engaged in describing the geology of many West Virginia counties. A number of these specimens were forwarded to David White for study, but Reger himself applied names to some of them.

One of his better known localities was in the Valley Head and Elkins sandstones of the Upper Devonian Chemung formation near Elkins, West Virginia, where he found several unusually large log-like objects. These he described at length as the "Tygart Valley Petrified Forest". The State designated the site as a place of historic interest, and caused a marker describing "Fossil Tree Park" to be erected in the early 1930's.

Unfortunately, no trace of the internal structure of the "trees" was ever found preserved, nor did they exhibit any diagnostic surface markings other than coarse surface corrugations. David White did not express a direct opinion about the "trees", but in the Letter of Transmittal accompanying the Randolph County Geologic Report, Sisler[12] reported that White entertained considerable doubt about them, and had expressed the idea that they were possibly sedimentation phenomena. Professor Chester A. Arnold, paleobotanist at the University of Michigan, was of the same opinion, in a paper published in 1937, after a brief

[10]Scudder, S. H. 1895. Revision of the American fossil cockroaches, with descriptions of new forms. *U. S. Geol. Surv. Bull.* 124, 176 pp.

[11]"A new fossil polypore (*Pseudopolyporus carbonicus*), Carboniferous, West Virginia. *Mycologia* 2:93, 94. 1910.

[12]James D. Sisler, "Letter of transmittal," *In* Reger, "Randolph County" *W. Va. Geol. Surv. County Rpts.* p. vi. 1931.

study of the structures. Dr. Richard Krausel of Germany generally subscribed to this same viewpoint in his paper[13] on the Upper Devonian flora of Elkins, West Virginia.

Of course, it would be impossible to list all of the talented amateur collectors, but the story would be incomplete without mention of Professor W. A. Bendrat (Beckley College in Beckley, Raleigh County), who collected in the difficult Pocahontas area. Some of his specimens were studied by Lou Williams at the University of Chicago. Several dozen others were donated to West Virginia University.

The period which we shall characterize as the Recent Years starts in the early 1930's after a considerable period during which no papers were published.

Although short-lived, this resurgence produced several important works. Oscar L. Haught, recently retired from the West Virginia Geological and Economic Survey, has collected quite extensively in West Virginia, although much of his material remains unpublished. His preliminary paper[14] concerning the flora of the Greene formation (Dunkard series) is the only recent one dealing with that difficult area. In addition to his own work, he personally guided the Dutch paleobotanist, the late W. J. Jongmans, on a field trip throughout southern West Virginia in 1933. This trip, an adjunct to the International Geological Congress meetings held in Washington, culminated in several papers by Jongmans, one of which was the first attempt to correlate the stratigraphic succession of North America with that of Europe.[15]

William Culp Darrah, while at Harvard University, collected

[13]Richard Krausel and Hermann Weyland. Pflanzenreste aus dem Devon von Nord-Amerika, I. Verbmerkung, von R. Krausel. II. Die oberdevonischen Floren von Elkins, West Virginia and Perry, Maine mit Beruckichtung einiger Strucke von der Chaleur-Bai, Canada, von Krausel and Weyland. Paleontographica, Band 86, avt. B, Leifrung 1-3, 78 p. 1941.

[14]"Characteristics of the flora of the Greene formation." *Proc. W. Va. Acad. Sci.* 7:83-87. 1934.

[15]Jongmans, W. J. and W. Gothan. 1933. Florenfolge und verleichende stratigrafie des karbons der ostlichen Staaten Nord-Amerika's vergleich mit West-Europa. Geol. Bur. Heerlen. Jaar-verslag Heerlen, 17-44.

[15]Jongmans, W. J. and W. Van der Gracht. 1935. Carboniferous floras of the United States and of western Europe. (abs.). Geol. Soc. Amer. Proc., 1934, p. 366.

[15]Jongmans, W. J., W. Gothan, and W. C. Darrah. 1937. Comparison of the floral succession in the Carboniferous of West Virginia with Europe. 2nd Cong. Strat. Carb., 1935, Heerlen. Compte Rendu Vol. I, p. 393-415.

[15]Jongmans, W. J. 1937. Some remarks on *Neuropteris ovata* in the American Carboniferous. 2nd Cong. Strat. Carb., 1935, Heerlen. Compte Rendu Vol. I, p. 417-422.

several times within West Virginia. In 1936 he led the French paleobotanist, Paul Bertrand, on a collecting trip throughout the area.

During the late 1930's and through the 1940's, interest in paleobotany waned, primarily due to the World War, and was not generally revived until about 1950 when Dr. Aureal T. Cross accepted a combined position with the Geology Department of West Virginia University and with the West Virginia Geological and Economic Survey. He came to this State after several years of intensive work in the coal measures of the eastern United States. He and his students have engaged in many critical studies on both the megaflora and microflora of the State, which ultimately will aid in producing an up-to-date listing of the fossil flora of West Virginia.

In addition to this localized effort, nearly all of the contemporary American paleobotanists have collected in the State during the last decade. Recent foreign visitors include the late Professor Birbal Sahni, founder of the Institute of Paleobotany at Lucknow, India, who visited West Virginia during a tour of the United States in 1951, and Dr. Hans Bode, of Muenster, West Germany, who made extended collecting trips, amounting to some two to three weeks time, in 1956 and again in 1959.

REFERENCES

BLIZZARD, WILLIAM C. "The Cranny Probers," *West Virginia Conservation* (July, 1962), 21-27.

BRYNER, CHARLES L. "Prophet without Honor: Life and Botanical Contributions of Edward Strieby Steele." *Diss. W. Va. Univ. Graduate School.* 1957.

CORE, EARL L. "The Botanical Exploration of West Virginia," *Proceedings West Virginia Academy of Science* 10:46-60. 1936.

CORE, EARL L. "Raymond H. Torrey," *Castanea* 4:6-7. 1939.

CORE, EARL L. "Joseph E. Harned," *Castanea* 16:78-79. 1951.

CORE, EARL L. *Outlines of the Flora of West Virginia.* Morgantown: West Virginia University Bookstore, 1954.

CORE, EARL L. *Plant Life of West Virginia.* New York: Scholar's Library, 1960.

MILLSPAUGH, C. F. *Botanical Field work in the State.* West Virginia Geological Survey 5(A). Wheeling: Wheeling News Litho. Company, 1913.

WHITE, DAVID. *The Fossil Flora of West Virginia.* West Virginia Geological Survey 5(A). Wheeling. 1913 (pp. 390-453).

Index

T

U

V

W

Y

Z